WORKBOOK 3

English
No Problem!

Jenni Currie Santamaría
ABC Adult School
Los Angeles Unified School District
Cerritos, CA

Mary Myers-Hall
ABC Adult School
Los Angeles Unified School District
Cerritos, CA

New Readers Press

English—No Problem!™
English—No Problem! Level 3 Workbook
ISBN 1-56420-363-8

Copyright © 2004 New Readers Press
New Readers Press
ProLiteracy's Publishing Division
104 Marcellus Street, Syracuse, New York 13204
www.newreaderspress.com

Printed in the United States of America
9 8 7 6 5 4

Proceeds from the sale of New Readers Press materials support professional
development, training, and technical assistance programs of ProLiteracy
that benefit local literacy programs in the U.S. and around the globe.

Acquisitions Editor: Paula L. Schlusberg
Developer: Mendoza and Associates
Project Director: Roseanne Mendoza
Project Editor: Pat Harrington-Wydell
Content Editor: Judi Lauber
Production Director: Heather Witt-Badoud
Designer: Kimbrly Koennecke
Illustrations: Carolyn Boehmer, Linda Tiff, James Wallace
Production Specialist: Jeffrey R. Smith
Cover Design: Kimbrly Koennecke
Cover Photography: Robert Mescavage Photography
Photo Credits: Hal Silverman Studio

Contents

Lesson 1 Activities for Young and Old

Exercise A   Rank these activities (1 to 8) in order of interest to you. Number 1 is your favorite activity to watch or do.

_____ martial arts

_____ chess

_____ crafts

_____ gymnastics

_____ cheerleading

_____ ceramics

_____ listening to a lecture

_____ aerobics

In your notebook, write a sentence about each activity. Start with your favorite activity. Here are some examples:

<u>I love to watch gymnastics in the Olympics.</u>

<u>I never learned how to play chess.</u>

Exercise B   Fill in the blanks in the questions and answers. The first one is done as an example.

1. What date _____*does*_____ the aerobics class _____*start*_____ ?

    It _____*starts*_____ on June 11.

2. How long _____ the ceramics class last?

    It _____ for one month.

3. How much _____ the lecture _____ ?

    It _____ $10.

4. Where _____ the martial arts class?

    It _____ in room 25.

Exercise C   Read the information about the pools and the class schedules.

Swim Instruction

Mayfair Pool opens Saturday, May 26, for swim sessions and will be open weekends throughout June. Daily swim sessions begin Friday, June 15, at Mayfair Pool. McCormick Pool opens Saturday, June 23. Daily operation ends at both McCormick and Mayfair Pools on Monday, September 3.

Splish Splash 50+ Water Exercise
This class improves strength and flexibility!
June 26-July 26 • Tues./Thurs. 8-9 a.m.
McCormick Pool
Instructor: McGinnis
Fee: $20

Tiny Tot Beginning Swimming
Ages 3-5. Parent must enter the water.
June 11-22 • Mon.-Wed. 3:30-4:00
Mayfair Pool
Instructor: Randall
Fee: $18

Write a phone conversation in your notebook. You are calling the Parks and Recreation office to find out about swimming classes for an older person and for a young child. Ask questions about the classes. The employee uses information from the schedule above to answer your questions. For example, you could start this way:

Employee: Mercer County Parks and Recreation. How can I help you?

Me: I want to find a swim class for my daughter.

Exercise D   Correct the mistakes in these sentences. Write the corrected sentences on the lines.

1. What time is the swimming class start?

    _____

2. The gymnastics class don't meet on July 4th.

    _____

3. How much the class costs?

    _____

4. When is the class finish?

    _____

Lesson 2 Conflict at the Office

Exercise A   Unscramble these sentences and write them on the lines below. Some of them are questions. Add correct punctuation. Use a capital letter where necessary. The first sentence is done as an example.

1. join / Annie / don't / basketball / to / team / wants / but / I / the

    Annie wants to join the basketball team, but I don't.

2. in / you / do / sports / participate

    _____

3. at / she / does / home / conflicts / have

    _____

4. are / person / a / confident / you

    _____

5. she / don't / I / has / confidence / but

    _____

6. fulfills / many / Senior / the / Center / needs

    _____

Exercise B   Fill in the blanks with *do, don't, does, doesn't, is, isn't,* or *aren't.*

1. My sister loves aerobics, but I _____ .

2. I'm not very athletic, but she _____ .

3. Swimming is easy for me, but aerobics _____ .

4. I like exercising alone, but she _____ .

5. I don't usually join clubs or groups, but she _____ .

6. She doesn't like to sew or do crafts, but I _____ .

7. Some sisters are very much alike, but we _____ .

> alike = the same

Exercise C   Use these words to fill in the blanks. Read the whole story
before you begin.

disrespectful	generations	respectful	unreliable
flexible	inflexible	responsible	

Mina works with a young woman named Trish. Sometimes Mina has a

hard time understanding Trish. She's not sure if it's because they have

different personalities or because they are from different

_____ . Mina knows that Trish is a good worker, but she
              1

doesn't like the way that she dresses. Mina always wears a suit or jacket

to the office, and she thinks that Trish's clothes look unprofessional. In Mina's opinion,

wearing jeans to work is _____ of other people's feelings. Trish disagrees.
                                   2

Trish thinks that Mina can't accept new ideas. She thinks that Mina is very

_____ because she doesn't like change.
              3

    In Trish's opinion, how people do their jobs is more important than how they look. She

doesn't work in the front office, so the customers never see her. She always arrives at work on

time and completes the jobs that she has to do. She feels that she is very

_____ . She also thinks that she is _____ of other people.
              4   5

She speaks politely and tries to be nice to everyone. She thinks that Mina should relax and be

more _____ . Trish says, "It doesn't matter what I wear. The important thing
              6

is that I always do my work. I'm not _____ or lazy. I'm a good employee!"
                                                7

Exercise D   Write sentences in your notebook about Trish
and Mina.

  Mina wears suits to work, but Trish doesn't.

One Step Up
In your notebook, describe a
reliable person that you know
and an irresponsible person
that you know. In your
sentences, give examples that
show why you think that the
person is reliable or
irresponsible.

Lesson 3 Sports to Play and Watch

Exercise A   Read the four paragraphs. Decide which title in the box belongs to each paragraph. Write the letter in the blank.

a. The Amazing Chess Master	**c.** Swimming Is the Best!
b. There's Nothing Like Soccer	**d.** I Can Sew You a Suit

_____ **1.** I do this every day because fitness is important. This exercise makes all of my muscles stronger, including my heart, but there's a very low risk of hurting my body. I usually do about 20 laps, and then I'm exhausted! I like this sport because I'm not very competitive and I don't like to play on teams. This is something I can do by myself whenever I have a chance to go to the gym. People who have their own pools are lucky!

_____ **2.** I should think more about fitness, but when it's time to relax, I prefer a puzzle, a good book, or this game. Although I've been playing it for many years, I still can't beat my father. I try hard to win because I'm very competitive, but somehow he always takes my queen. I have even tried reading the advice column in the paper about the best moves. This is the most challenging game that I know of, at least mentally, and I love to play.

_____ **3.** I have been doing this since I was quite young, and I find it both relaxing and rewarding. I can't just sit and watch TV or talk without keeping my hands busy, and I love the satisfaction of making something and seeing what it looks like when I'm finished. My children appreciate my skill, too!

_____ **4.** I like competition, and I care about keeping fit, but the most important thing to me is just having fun. I'm a team player. For me, there's nothing better than getting together with my friends in the park on Saturday morning and trying to beat the other team. We meet every week unless it's raining. Sometimes we win and sometimes we lose, but we always have a good time.

In-Class Extension   In your notebook, write a short description of something you like to do. Don't name the activity. Read the description to your group and ask them to guess what the activity is.

Exercise B Read the three sentences. One of them is a main idea. Two
of them are supporting ideas. Write *M* next to the main idea. Write *S* next
to the supporting ideas. The first sentence is done as an example.

1. _S_ At family card games, we both get mad if we lose.

   _____ I get very competitive with my brother.

   _____ At school, we always compare our test scores.

2. _____ It's easy to fall off the bars if you are careless.

   _____ If you do an exercise before your muscles are ready, you
   can hurt yourself.

   _____ Gymnastics can be risky if you aren't careful.

3. _____ Making crafts can be very challenging.

   _____ Sometimes the instructions look easy, but they are difficult.

   _____ Certain materials are difficult to work with.

4. _____ I like to do difficult puzzles.

   _____ I always enjoy challenges.

   _____ When something is broken, I try to fix it.

Exercise C Write a main-idea sentence with each word. Write one
supporting idea for each main idea.

1. (challenge) _____

   _____

2. (fitness) _____

   _____

3. (competitive) _____

   _____

4. (team) _____

   _____

5. (risky) _____

   _____

Looking at Your Goals   Think back on your goals for this unit.

How well can you . . .	Not very well		Somewhat		Very well
ask for information over the phone?	1	2	3	4	5
express agreement and disagreement?	1	2	3	4	5
talk to people about your interests?	1	2	3	4	5
understand phone recordings?	1	2	3	4	5
explain how to do an activity?	1	2	3	4	5
another goal:_____	1	2	3	4	5

Learning about Opportunities for People of All Ages

Think back on the lessons.

What was the most important thing you learned about opportunities
for people of all ages?

_____

_____

What do you still need to learn about these kinds of opportunities?
List one or two things.

_____

_____

Improving Your English   In this unit you studied these things. Check the
ones that have improved.

_____ using words that describe people and
activities

_____ asking and answering questions in the
present tense

_____ using compound sentences

_____ pronouncing contrasting sounds

_____ linking consonant and vowel sounds

_____ listening for details in a phone
recording

_____ reading for the main idea in an
advertisement

_____ reading for the main idea in a letter

_____ _____
another thing that you improved

Lesson 1 Body Language

Exercise A Write the correct word on each line.

1. To _____ is to quickly close and re-open one eye. It's

bow / wink / nudge

an informal gesture that means "You and I understand something."

2. To _____ is to move your shoulders up and down. It's

wink / shrug / slouch

an informal gesture that means "I don't know" or possibly "I don't care."

3. To _____ is to bend at the waist. In the US, this is done at the end of a

bow / stare / whisper

performance. Men may also do this before a formal dance.

4. To _____ is to sit or stand with your shoulders bent. It means that you are

whistle / shrug / slouch

tired, sad, or bored.

5. To _____ is to look for a long time. It is not polite to do this to people.

stare / whisper / wink

6. To _____ is to speak in a quiet voice so that people cannot hear you.

stare / whisper / wink

7. To _____ is to touch someone with one elbow.

stare / slouch / nudge

Exercise B Choose the simple past or past continuous tense for each
sentence. Fill in the blanks with the correct word or words.

Last week, Jae Lee's neighbor, Petra, _____ her little dog in the backyard.

1. was leaving / left

But she didn't lock the gate, and when she _____ home, her puppy wasn't

2. was getting / got

there. Petra was worried, and she _____ out the door to look for her puppy.

3. was running / ran

Just then, Jae Lee came over. He _____ her puppy. Petra was so grateful that

4. was carrying / carried

she _____ her arms around him. When she did that, her neighbor backed

5. was throwing / threw

away from her. Petra _____ that he was offended. The next day, she

6. was thinking / thought

_____ in her kitchen, and she _____ the doorbell ring. Her

7. was sitting / sat   8. was hearing / heard

neighbor was at the door. He smiled and said, "Hi. Can I talk to you for a minute?"

Exercise C   Underline all the examples of body language in the article.

Body Language

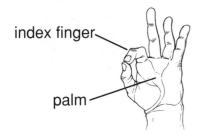

index finger

palm

Body language and gestures are different in different countries. It's easy to be confused or to offend someone if you don't understand gestures. For example, in the US, making a circle with the thumb and index finger and showing the palm means "OK." But in many Latin American countries, this gesture is offensive, and in Japan, a similar gesture means "money."

In the US, the gesture for "come here" is with the palm facing up, sometimes with the index finger extended. In some Asian countries, this gesture is considered rude. In many countries, the gesture for "come here" is made with the palm facing down, but in the US, this gesture looks disrespectful. In the US, people usually point at things (but not at people) with the index finger. In many countries, this way of pointing is not polite, and people point with their chins. People in the US may not know that you are pointing if you use your chin.

Some body-language communication problems are more likely to happen in the home. For example, in many Buddhist countries, it is offensive to show the bottom of your feet. But in the US, many people put their feet on a stool when they are sitting, and sometimes they cross one foot over a knee. These positions are informal, but not rude.

Every culture has different rules about the dinner table, and it's a good idea to learn the table manners of your host before you visit. In some cultures, people leave food on their plates because an empty plate means that they want more food. But in the US, if you leave much food on your plate, your host might think you didn't like the meal!

Lesson 2 A Simple Apology

Exercise A Read the paragraph about Jae Lee's problem at work. The
angry customer is telling the story. This paragraph needs more punctuation.
In your notebook, copy the paragraph. Put in the correct punctuation for
direct speech. Remember to use commas, quotation marks, and capital letters.

      I was so mad last week when I went to Lee's Dry Cleaners to pick
up my jacket. <u>I gave the clerk my ticket</u>, and she looked for my jacket.
After a few minutes, <u>she said I'm sorry, but your jacket won't be ready</u>
until Thursday. I couldn't believe it because I knew <u>she told me that it</u>
<u>would be ready on Tuesday</u>. I started to yell at her. I said you told me
Tuesday, not Thursday! <u>The manager came out</u> when <u>I was yelling</u>. He
said is there a problem that I can help you with? So I told him about the
mix-up. He said pardon me for the misunderstanding. Then <u>he looked at</u>
<u>the ticket</u> and said you can see that Thursday is circled, not Tuesday. I
was so embarrassed when I found out that it was my fault. I said oh,
you're right. I apologize for yelling. I didn't look at the ticket. He was
very nice about it. He said don't worry, we'll call you when your jacket
is ready. Again, please forgive us for the misunderstanding.

Exercise B On the time line below, write the underlined events in the
order that they happened. The first event is written as an example.

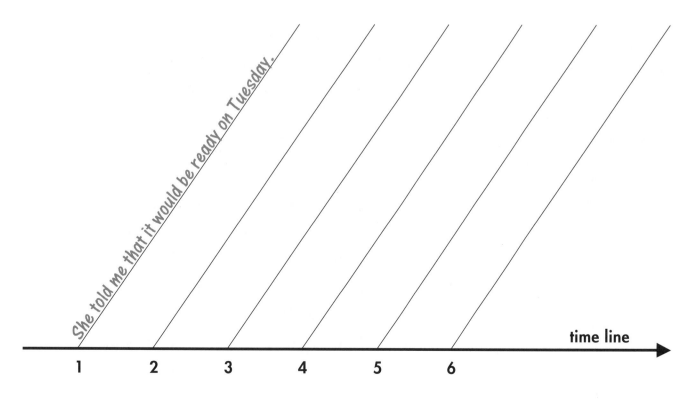

Exercise C   Look at the vocabulary words below. Write apologies, using the vocabulary words in your sentences. One apology is written as an example.

1. (apology, fault) _I'm sorry. Please accept my apology. It's really my fault._

2. (pardon me, expect) _____

3. (excuse me, misunderstanding) _____

4. (forgive me, offend) _____

5. (apologize, mix-up) _____

6. (gesture, offensive) _____

Exercise D   The words below are hidden in this puzzle. Words may be written forwards, backwards, across, down, or diagonally. Circle the words in the puzzle. Write a sentence with each word in your notebook.

apology	concerned	gesture	resolution	whistle
back away	expectation	misunderstand	shrug	
body language	fault	offend	whisper	

```
d o h o f f e n d t t n f b c r e d e g s x
n b g h h r c d e d r e a h j k l u e h e c
b d n t r s h r u g b l u j k j a e g f g e
e e o e a s e r d m b i l v r a c b a n w p
n n i c q h o p u i m v t i o p y b u b h b
u r t r d u m y o s t b k n g o l r g s i n
b e a v e g e s t u r e k o k l n n n x s e
c c t n u y l m h n j k u o p o p k a k p m
m n c u i w y r v d u y e w b g c x l p e y
o o e i u n h v f e r e r p l y i n y b r f
h c p t r e w i n r d p m n b f d s d w i u
k i x t r e w q s s r e s o l u t i o n l u
n b e d f e r t y t i o k j t r e h b k l o
m j h b g r f e d a l u i o p l m j h r g b
c v c h y k i o l n n e b a c k a w a y d e
o p i y b h g t r d j n b v f d j k l r e c
```

Lesson 3 In Public

Exercise A   Write sentences using the words in paretheses to describe the people in the pictures. Write the letter of a picture next to the number. Explain why you think the words describe the people. One has been done as an example.

a.    b.    c.    d.

_b_ **1.** (rude) _The girl is rude. She is licking her fingers._____

_____ **2.** (impatient) _____

_____ **3.** (aggressive) _____

_____ **4.** (polite) _____

_____ **5.** (impolite) _____

Exercise B   Choose one of the pictures from Exercise A and write a story about it. Use your imagination. Include direct speech to report what people said. Here is an example:

_Picture a: The woman was at a party and she saw her friend. He came to say_____

_hello. He stood very close to her because the people at the party were making_____

_a lot of noise. He said, "Are you having fun?"_____

Exercise C   Look at the list of actions. Write sentences explaining when it's OK and when it's rude to do these things. One has been done as an example.

1. (whisper) _It's OK to whisper in a library. It's rude to whisper at the dinner table._

2. (interrupt) _____

3. (stare) _____

4. (whistle) _____

5. (snap your fingers) _____

6. (cut in line) _____

Exercise D   Read the following letter of apology from the manager of a furniture company to a customer.

Dear Mrs. Rose,

    Please accept our apology for the misunderstanding about the delivery date of your sofa. Customer satisfaction is very important to us, and I hope you'll excuse us for the miscommunication. I apologize for any problems that this delivery mix-up caused you. To help resolve this problem, I'm going to remove the delivery fee from your bill. You are a valued customer, and we hope to see you again soon at The Furniture Palace.

Sincerely,

Steve Marsh

Steve Marsh
Customer Service Manager

Choose one of the situations below, or create your own, and write a letter of apology in your notebook. Use words from the Lesson 2 vocabulary list.

1. You made a mistake at work. Write an apology to a customer. Explain the reason for the mistake and tell how you would like to resolve the problem.

2. You didn't come to class for three weeks and you didn't tell your teacher. Write an apology to your teacher. Include an explanation for your absence.

Use an idea map like this to prepare for writing.

Check your writing:

- Did you put a comma after *Dear _____* and *Sincerely?*
- Did you indent the first sentence?
- Did you use simple past and past continuous correctly?

Looking at Your Goals   Think back on your goals for this unit.

How well can you . . .	Not very well		Somewhat		Very well
understand social situations in the US?	1	2	3	4	5
explain reasons for conflicts?	1	2	3	4	5
apologize for mistakes?	1	2	3	4	5
write a short letter?	1	2	3	4	5
understand and describe gestures and body language?	1	2	3	4	5
another goal:_____	1	2	3	4	5

Learning about Dealing with Miscommunication   Think back on the lessons.

What was the most important thing you learned about dealing with miscommunication?

_____

_____

What do you still need to learn about dealing with miscommunication? List one or two things.

_____

_____

Improving Your English   In this unit you studied these things. Check the ones that have improved.

_____ describing conflicts and resolutions

_____ using the past continuous and simple past

_____ reporting direct speech

_____ stressing the correct syllable

_____ using stress in positive and negative sentences

_____ reading e-mail messages for a purpose

_____ reading an order form for details

_____ understanding everyday conversations

_____ _____
another thing that you improved

Lesson 1 Safety on the Job

Exercise A Change the sentences to questions. The first one has been done as an example.

1. She tripped over her shoelaces. _Did she trip over her shoelaces?_

2. He knocked over the lamp. _____

3. They were suspicious of him. _____

4. The little girl fractured her arm. _____

5. The doctor treated the injury. _____

6. She got a shock from the old cord. _____

7. The plant was poisonous. _____

Exercise B Read the paragraph. Write questions and answers below. The first one has been done as an example.

After Miguel burned his hand, he noticed a lot of safety problems at the restaurant. People often left open bottles on the counter near the grill. Sometimes the floors were slippery because employees were too busy to clean up after a spill. He saw an unplugged cord lying on the floor. When he looked for the first-aid kit, he finally found it in the bottom of a drawer. Miguel decided to make his workplace safer.

1. (What / on the floor) _What was lying on the floor?_

   An unplugged cord was lying on the floor.

2. (What / look for) _____

   _____

3. (Where / find it) _____

   _____

4. (What / decide) _____

   _____

Exercise C   Use the words in the box on the right to fill in the crossword puzzle. Be sure that your answer fits in the puzzle before you go on to the next sentence!

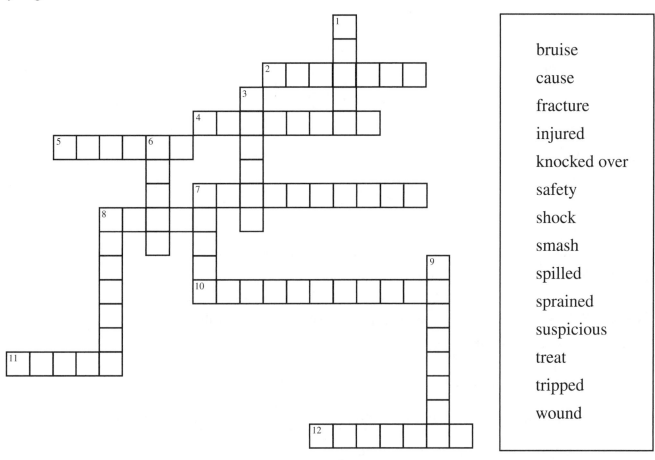

bruise

cause

fracture

injured

knocked over

safety

shock

smash

spilled

sprained

suspicious

treat

tripped

wound

Across

2. Before I _____ my knee, I went jogging every day.

4. He _____ his ankle when he fell down.

5. You should think about _____ at work and at home.

7. The policeman was _____ of the robber.

8. Did she _____ her finger in the car door?

10. When she _____ the glass, water spilled everywhere.

11. You should put a bandage on that open _____ .

12. After I _____ over the cord, I put it away.

Down

1. They don't know the _____ of the accident.

3. She got a big purple _____ on her arm.

6. You should ask the doctor to _____ your injury.

7. He got a _____ when he put his knife in the toaster.

8. Oh no! I _____ my coffee!

9. Did you _____ or sprain your ankle?

Lesson 2 Safety at Home

Exercise A   Match the pairs to make safety words and expressions from the lesson. The first one has been done as an example.

_d_ 1. un   a. detector

_____ 2. put   b. route

_____ 3. smoke   c. up

_____ 4. re   d. plug

_____ 5. plug   e. in

_____ 6. lock   f. away

_____ 7. escape   g. extinguisher

_____ 8. fire   h. place

Write the words or expressions in your notebook. Put an accent mark over the most stressed syllable in each word or expression.

Exercise B   Read the paragraph. Circle the correct words. Then copy the complete paragraph into your notebook.

No one expects household accidents to happen. We all think

that our houses are very | **1.** safe   poisonous   slippery |. But accidents

are a common cause of death and | **2.** prevention   robbery   injury |,

especially for children. Of course, the best way to

| **3.** cause   suspect   prevent | accidents is to fix any problems that might

| **4.** cause   prevent   suspect | accidents. You may not think your

cleaners are | **5.** valuables   poisons   injuries |, but they are

| **6.** poisonous   safe   suspicious | if a child drinks them. Are they in a

safe place? Is there a mat in the bathtub so that nobody

| **7.** slips   robs   goes off | ? Are the windows and doors locked when

you're away so that no one can | **8.** prevent   injure   rob | the house?

Take a look around. A little bit of | **9.** robbery   poison   prevention |

can save you a lot of pain!

Exercise C   Read the story about a fire that happened in Miguel's neighborhood.

Neighborhood Fire

Experts at the scene of an apartment fire at 3918 N. Mason Avenue are still trying to find the cause of last night's blaze. The fire injured 19 people and sent a 6-year-old boy to the hospital, suffering from smoke inhalation.

Antonio Salazar was trapped in a back room at the time of the fire. His parents, Claudia and Juan Salazar, ran out of the building with their 2-year-old twins after they heard an explosion. They thought Antonio was right behind them.

When they realized their oldest son was not with them, they began to panic. "I was really scared when I looked up and didn't see my boy," said Juan Salazar, a restaurant manager. Through tears, Claudia Salazar said, "I was so relieved after the firefighter rescued our little boy. We'll never forget this night as long as we live."

The fire was reported by a neighbor who called 911 when the explosion woke him up.

This story does not tell events in the order that they happened. What happened first? Number the events from first (1) to last (5).

_____ The Salazar family realized that their son was not with them.

_____ A firefighter rescued the boy.

_____ Experts investigated the fire.

_____ A neighbor called to report the fire.

_____ Antonio Salazar went to the hospital.

Exercise D   Think about the story in Exercise C. Make sentences using words from each part of the box. Write each sentence in your notebook.

1. Juan Salazar woke up	**before**	he was injured.
2. Claudia Salazar was very frightened		their son got out.
3. The boy went to the hospital	**when**	he heard an explosion.
4. The parents ran out of the building		her son was rescued.
5. The firefighters arrived	**after**	the neighbor called them.

Lesson 3 At the Bus Stop

Exercise A   Complete the story with words and expressions from the box.
Use the correct verb tenses.

break into	keep an eye on	stranger	victim	witness

Miguel helped to make his neighborhood safer. When his neighbors went on vacation, he

_____ their houses while they were away. If he saw a _____ ,

1
he watched to make sure the person didn't try to _____ someone's house or

3
car. He had already been a _____ to one crime when he saw the purse

4
snatching, and he certainly didn't ever want to be a _____ !

5

Exercise B   Read the paragraph about Miguel's co-worker Paula.

Three days ago, Paula saw a <u>stranger</u> near her neighbors'
house. The man broke into a bedroom window when they were
not home. Paula called 911. Two police cars came immediately.
They caught the suspect and put him in the police car. A few
days later, one of Paula's neighbors was <u>mugged</u> while she was
walking down the street. Her purse was <u>stolen</u>. She described
the man who did it, but the police didn't have any <u>suspects</u>. A few days
later, a <u>robbery</u> happened in the neighborhood. Paula and her neighbors
decided that they had to do something to make their neighborhood safer.
Paula talked to the police about starting a Neighborhood Watch program.
A police officer met with Paula and her neighbors to help them get started.

Write past-tense questions and answers about this story. Use the underlined
words in your questions or answers. The first one has been done as an
example.

1.   *Who did Paula see near her neighbors' house? She saw a stranger.* _____

2.   _____

3.   _____

4.   _____

5.   _____

Exercise C   Circle the word that is different.

1. held   taken   stolen   grabbed

2. judge   victim   witness   stranger

3. watch   lock up   look at   keep an eye on

4. meet   suspect   introduce   get to know

Exercise D   Think about your home, school, workplace, and neighborhood. Do any of these places have safety problems? Use the idea map to prepare for writing. In the center circle, write *Home, Work, School,* or *Neighborhood.* Brainstorm examples of what is safe and unsafe in that place.

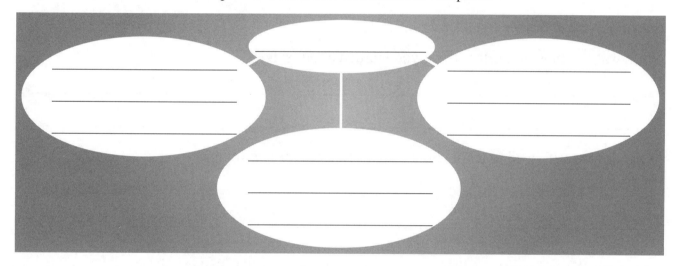

In your notebook, write a paragraph about the topic in your center circle. Start with a main-idea sentence that tells whether you think the place needs many, few, or no safety changes. Describe what is already safe there. Then describe the things that you need to do to make it safer. One student wrote this for a main idea:

My school is usually safe, but there are a few safety problems.

Check your writing:

- Have you used safety words correctly?
- Do the details in your paragraph explain your main idea?
- Have you used commas, periods, and capital letters correctly?

In-Class Extension   Read your safety paragraph to a partner. Listen to your partner's paragraph. Give your partner some advice on what to do about the safety problems. Listen to your partner's advice.

Looking at Your Goals   Think back on your goals for this unit.

How well can you . . .	Not very well		Somewhat		Very well
report an accident in English?	1	2	3	4	5
prevent injuries at work?	1	2	3	4	5
make your home safe?	1	2	3	4	5
help make your neighborhood safe?	1	2	3	4	5
report a crime in English?	1	2	3	4	5
another goal:_____	1	2	3	4	5

Learning about Safety   Think back on the lessons.

What was the most important thing you learned about safety?

_____

_____

What do you still need to learn about safety? List one or two things.

_____

_____

Improving Your English   In this unit you studied these things. Check the
ones that have improved.

_____ understanding safety words

_____ pronouncing past tense verb
endings *(-ed)*

_____ stressing important words

_____ asking and answering questions in
the past tense

_____ locating information on a form

_____ using *when, before,* and *after* in
sentences

_____ reading for details in a brochure

_____ listening for details in a conversation

_____ _____
another thing that you improved

Lesson 1 Decisions! Decisions!

Exercise A   Read the story about Olivia and answer the questions with complete sentences. The first question has been done as an example.

Olivia had been looking for health insurance before she got her new job with Aptel. She was so happy when she found out that Aptel offered health benefits. Before she began working there, she didn't have health insurance. Her last employer didn't offer it. Victor lost his job two years ago and started his own business, so he didn't have health insurance either.

When Victor broke his leg, they had to pay cash for the ambulance, emergency care, hospital stay, and follow-up doctor visits. It was very expensive. They had to borrow money to pay for everything. Before his accident, they knew that medical coverage was important, but they couldn't afford private insurance.

When Olivia first talked to Victor about getting health insurance through her company, he didn't think that they could afford the monthly payments. She reminded him how much money they had to pay for medical bills when he injured his leg. After he thought about it, he agreed that it would be better to make small payments every month. They decided to enroll in the health plan.

Olivia wants to see a chiropractor very soon for her neck pain, and she knows that she needs glasses. She hasn't had her vision checked for two years, so she wants to do it right away. She has already decided what kind of frames she wants for her new glasses!

1. Why didn't Olivia and Victor have health insurance before?

   They didn't have insurance because their jobs didn't offer it.

2. Why did Olivia and Victor have to borrow money?

   _____

3. Why didn't Victor want to pay for the new health insurance at first?

   _____

4. Why did they enroll in the health plan?

   _____

5. Why does Olivia want to see a chiropractor?

   _____

Exercise B   Read the letter about the insurance policy. Write answers to the questions. Use complete sentences.

Dear Mr. and Mrs. Morales,

　　It has come to my attention that you are researching your health insurance options. I'd like to give you some information about a new Sana Delta policy. If you are under age 50, emergency health coverage in the case of an accident or sudden illness is available for you and your children under 18 years old. The yearly premium is divided into twelve easy payments of one hundred dollars each, and the deductible is three hundred dollars per year. Yearly physical exams and doctor visits can be included for an additional charge.

　　I also have policies to cover your home, car, and all of your insurance needs. Please call me if you would like me to meet with you to discuss details.

Looking forward to meeting you,

Sal Mosqueda

Sal Mosqueda

---

1. Who is eligible? _____

   _____

2. What does the policy cover? _____

   _____

3. How much are monthly payments? _____

   _____

4. How much is the yearly premium? _____

   _____

5. How much is the deductible? _____

   _____

6. Who is the agent? _____

   _____

Lesson 2 Protecting Your Home

Exercise A Read the paragraph. Circle the correct words.

If people want financial security, they 1. have to don't have to

must not forget the importance of protecting themselves and their

belongings with insurance. Everyone needs some kind of health insurance

because anyone can get sick or have an accident. Most homeowners are

paying a bank loan, and they 2. have to don't have to must not have

home insurance because the bank requires it. Renters, however,

3. have to don't have to must not buy insurance. The landlord's

policy covers most damage that can happen to the building, but the

landlord 4. has to doesn't have to must not pay for the renter's

damaged or destroyed property.

Exercise B The underlined part of the sentence is an example of one of the
vocabulary words. Write the letter of each vocabulary word next to the
correct sentence. Note: The vocabulary words cannot replace the underlined
words in these sentences.

_____ **1.** Nicole came home and found her living room floor
<u>covered with water</u>.

_____ **2.** She had an <u>expensive collection</u> of plates.

_____ **3.** She had some of her great-grandmother's beautiful
<u>old furniture</u>.

_____ **4.** She dropped a glass and it <u>broke into a hundred pieces</u>.

_____ **5.** She <u>spilled some soda on the sofa</u>, and she couldn't get the
stain out.

_____ **6.** It's a good thing she had insurance to cover
<u>everything she owned</u>.

_____ **7.** Someone <u>broke into her friend's house and smashed the TV</u>.

_____ **8.** They also <u>took her jewelry</u>, but it wasn't very expensive.

a. antiques

b. belongings

c. damage

d. destroy

e. flood

f. theft

g. valuables

h. vandalism

Exercise C Read the article about buying homeowners insurance.

Buying Homeowners
INSURANCE

Choosing the right homeowners insurance policy can be very difficult. Here are some tips to help you:

▶ Ask how much it would cost to rebuild your home. Many people insure their house only for the amount they paid. That is probably not enough insurance. You need to insure your home for the amount that it would cost to rebuild it. Your insurance agent can help you in deciding the amount of insurance you really need. Review your policy every year because prices go up!

▶ Ask about flood insurance coverage. Most homeowners insurance policies do not cover flood damage. Your insurance agent can help you find a good policy to cover damage from floods. Or you can contact the Federal Insurance Administration and ask about the National Flood Insurance Program.

▶ Ask about the deductible amounts. Sometimes you can save money on your premiums by having higher deductibles.

▶ Make a list of your personal belongings. Take photographs or a videotape of everything you own. Collecting this information now can save you a lot of trouble in the future!

In your notebook, rewrite the advice from the article. Use *have to, don't have to, must,* and *must not* in your sentences. Write five sentences. Here is an example:

You have to ask how much it would cost to rebuild your home.

Exercise D Add commas, periods, and capital letters to this paragraph. You may need to review grammar from Units 1, 2, and 3.

Olivia called the insurance agent because she wanted to find out about homeowners insurance when she talked to the agent he also gave her some information about life insurance she learned that there are two kinds of life insurance *term* insurance is not very expensive when you are young but it gets expensive when you are older *whole-life* insurance is more expensive because it lasts your whole life the insurance agent wanted Olivia to buy life insurance but she didn't think she needed it she and Victor are both working and they don't have children yet she said to the insurance agent "maybe I will talk to you about life insurance after we have children"

Lesson 3 Saving for a Rainy Day

Exercise A Read the information from the bank flyer.

Account Types		
Statement Savings	under $1,000	2.23%
	$1,000-$9,999.99	2.47%
	$10,000 and over	3.45%
Money Market	under $1,000	1.98%
	$1,000-$9,999.99	2.23%
	$10,000 and over	3.20%
CD—30 day	$1,000 minimum deposit	2.75%
CD—60 day	$1,000 minimum deposit	2.75%
CD—90 day	$1,000 minimum deposit	3.00%
*If your account falls below the minimum balance any day of the month, a penalty will be charged for the month. The interest rate may change at any time, except for the Certificate of Deposit accounts, which have a fixed (unchanging) rate for the term of the CD.		

Use the information from the flyer to fill in the sentences below with these
words in the box.

certificate of deposit	interest rate	money market	penalty

1. The _____ for a statement savings account with more than $10,000 is 3.45%.

2. If you get a 30-day _____ , the interest will not change for 30 days.

3. The _____ accounts pay the lowest interest.

4. If your account falls below the minimum balance, you will pay a _____ .

Exercise B In your notebook, write a conversation between a customer and
a teller. The customer asks three questions about the savings accounts, and
the teller answers the questions with information from the bank flyer. Here is
an example:

Customer: Can you tell me the minimum deposit for a 30-day CD?

Teller: The minimum deposit is $1,000.

In-Class Extension Practice your conversation with a partner.

Exercise C Unscramble these sentences and write them on the lines below. Add correct punctuation. Use a capital letter where necessary.

1. it / to / fix / the / the / we / hail / damaged / had / because / roof

_____

2. retirement / because / we / enjoying / we / for / it / are / prepared / our

_____

3. security / would / have / everybody / like / to / financial

_____

Exercise D   Write a paragraph to answer <u>one</u> of these questions. Use *because* and *have to*. Use the idea map to help you write your paragraph. Write your main idea in the center circle. Write supporting ideas in the other circles.

- Have you ever given money to someone on the street? Why or why not?
- Should children get an allowance (weekly money) from their parents? How much?
- If you are saving money for something, what are you saving it for?

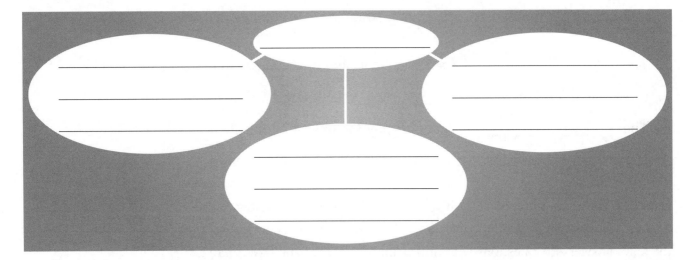

Check your writing:

- Did you indent the first sentence?
- Did you use *because* and *have to* correctly?
- Do your supporting sentences help to explain your main idea?

Looking at Your Goals   Think back on your goals for this unit.

How well can you . . .	Not very well		Somewhat		Very well
understand health insurance policies?	1	2	3	4	5
understand renters and homeowners insurance policies?	1	2	3	4	5
use names of medical specialists?	1	2	3	4	5
ask for information about savings accounts?	1	2	3	4	5
compare different kinds of savings accounts?	1	2	3	4	5
another goal:_____	1	2	3	4	5

Learning about Financial Planning   Think back on the lessons.

What was the most important thing you learned about
financial planning?

_____

_____

What do you still need to learn about financial planning?
List one or two things.

_____

_____

Improving Your English   In this unit you studied these things. Check the
ones that have improved.

_____ using financial planning words

_____ using sentences with *because*

_____ using *have to, must,* and *have got to*

_____ using choice intonation

_____ pronouncing schwa ("uh" sound) in
unstressed syllables

_____ reading for details about medical
benefits

_____ listening for details about insurance

_____ reading bank flyers

_____ _____
another thing that you improved

Lesson 1 Getting the Most for Your Money

Exercise A Read the story about Trevor's office equipment.

Trevor has a lot of office equipment in his home office. He bought a file cabinet 10 years ago. It has five large drawers for filing. At that time, he kept all of his records in it. After a while, it was difficult to keep track of everything. So he bought a computer two years ago. It's much easier now to find the information he needs in the computer files. He still keeps files in the file cabinet, but they're not very organized.

He has an old typewriter that he doesn't use anymore. He does all of his typing on the computer. He just bought a new printer. It's quiet and fast, and it has a three-year warranty. The old printer had a three-month warranty. It stopped working after one year, but the warranty had already run out.

keep track of = know about

He has two telephones in the office. The large, black phone hangs on the wall. It's eight years old. He also has a new lightweight portable phone with an answering machine. He bought it six months ago.

Write sentences about the items in Trevor's office. Use comparatives and superlatives. Two sentences have been done as examples.

1. <u>The file cabinet is the biggest item in the office.</u>

2. <u>The computer is more efficient than the typewriter.</u>

3. _____

4. _____

5. _____

6. _____

7. _____

8. _____

Exercise B Look at the following cassette recorder warranty card.

LIMITED WARRANTY
Model No. PL-TA703

You have just bought one of the best mini-cassette recorders available today. If the recorder is not in perfect condition, or if for any reason you are not satisfied and would like a refund or exchange, just return your recorder, with your sales receipt, to the store where you purchased it within 30 days. Trisonic America, Inc. guarantees the quality of this product as follows:

1. For 90 days from the original date of purchase, Trisonic will repair the defective product at no cost to you, or replace the defective product with a new one.
2. In addition, Trisonic will replace the defective parts for one year from the date of purchase.

You must send the item to Trisonic at the address on the other side of this card. Please package the item carefully to prevent damage. You must include your receipt for the item and a description of the problem.

WHAT WE WILL NOT COVER
This warranty does not cover items that have been repaired by anyone except Trisonic. It does not cover items that have been used incorrectly. It also does not cover batteries or cords.

THIS WARRANTY IS VALID ONLY IN THE USA.

Choose the correct word to complete each sentence. Write the letter of your choice on the line. The first one has been done as an example.

_b_ **1.** This _____ is good for one year.

     a. quality   b. warranty   c. purchase   d. condition

_____ **2.** Trisonic will _____ your money if you aren't happy with the recorder.

     a. warranty   b. guarantee   c. exchange   d. refund

_____ **3.** Trisonic will repair the recorder if it is _____ .

     a. quality   b. condition   c. defective   d. guarantee

_____ **4.** Trisonic _____ that you will be happy with the recorder.

     a. guarantees   b. warranties   c. conditions   d. refunds

_____ **5.** If your recorder is in bad _____ , Trisonic will repair it for you.

     a. quality   b. defective   c. condition   d. refund

_____ **6.** Bring your receipt if you want to _____ your recorder for a new one.

     a. guarantee   b. exchange   c. refund   d. warranty

Lesson 2 Second-Hand Rose

Exercise A   Unscramble the sentences about the Granville family and write them on the lines below. Add correct punctuation. Use a capital letter where necessary.

1. wasn't / want / dress / because / the / Tremaine / it / didn't / perfect

_____

2. decided / mind / dress / the / buy / Tremaine / her / and / changed / to

_____

3. Tremaine / to / Gail / Second-Hand Rose / went / and / yesterday

_____

4. a / flaw / dress / beautiful / they / had / found / that / a

_____

5. defect / showed / the / Gail / was / Tremaine / that / small

_____

In your notebook, write a paragraph by copying the sentences in the correct order. Remember to indent.

Exercise B   Use the words to fill in the blanks.

exchange	guarantee	refund	rip	scratch

   When Trevor got a new mirror, he brought it home carefully. But when he took it out of the bag, he discovered a _____ in the package, and a large _____

along the bottom of the mirror. He didn't see any _____ written on the
                                                                    3
package, but he decided to take the mirror back to the store. At first, he asked for an

_____ , but the store didn't have any more of the same kind of mirror. Then he
          4
asked for a _____ so that he could buy a mirror at a different store.
                        5

Exercise C Look at the pictures of Tremaine's clothing and accessories.

Write sentences about why Tremaine wants to buy new clothing and accessories. The first one has been done as an example.

1. _She wants to buy a new skirt because her old one is ripped._

2. _____

3. _____

4. _____

Exercise D Read these sentences. Underline the simple past verbs.

• Before Tremaine was born, Gail and Trevor bought most of their clothes at the mall.

• They liked shopping at the big department stores.

• They purchased their first sofa on credit.

• In fact, they paid for many things with credit.

• They made small payments every month.

• After a while, they had a lot of debt to pay.

• So they decided to use cash for all their purchases.

• They are sorry that they spent so much money on interest.

In these sentences, there are five simple past verbs that can be changed to *used to*. Rewrite the sentences with *used to* in your notebook.

Exercise E In your notebook, write sentences about things that you used to do but don't do anymore.

One Step Up
Read your sentences to your group. Tell why you don't do these things anymore.

Lesson 3 Bargain Hunting

Exercise A Fill in the names of the items in the graph.

Items Sold at the Community Garage Sale*

Name of Item

_____

_____

_____

_____

_____

_____

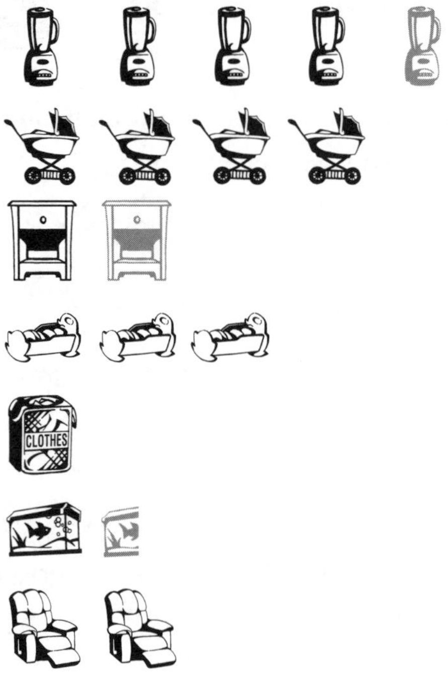

Each picture represents two items.   ▨ Items sold by the Granville family

Exercise B Choose the correct answer to each question. Write the letter of your choice on the line.

_____ **1.** Which item did they sell the most of at the community garage sale?

 a. recliners   b. strollers   c. blenders   d. nightstands

_____ **2.** How many cribs did they sell?

 a. three   b. six   c. nine   d. twelve

_____ **3.** How many aquariums did they sell?

 a. one   b. two   c. three   d. four

_____ **4.** How many items did the Granvilles sell?

 a. three   b. four   c. five   d. six

Exercise C Use these words to fill in the blanks. You can use a word more than once.

best	cheaper	more	most	than	the

Trevor: I finally chose the new printer that I'm going to buy for the business. It's so much

better _____ the old one.

                                       1

Gail: Tell me about it.

Trevor: Well, it was the _____ efficient one that I could find, and it

                                       2

had the _____ warranty.

                        3

Gail: That's nice, dear. We found a dress for Tremaine today. It's

_____ cutest thing you ever saw!

                        4

Trevor: I hope the price was better _____ the ones we saw last weekend.

                                       5

Gayle: Well, it was _____ expensive than I expected, but it was a lot

                               6

_____ than a new one!

                        7

Exercise D Use a Venn diagram to prepare for writing. Write your ideas about different kinds of places where people shop in your home country and in the US. Use this diagram as a model:

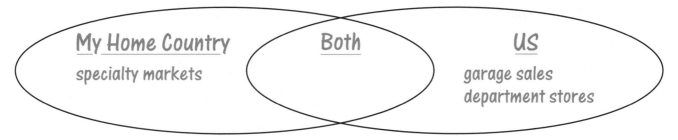

Write a paragraph in your notebook. Compare shopping in your home country to shopping in the US. Remember to state your main idea at the beginning of your paragraph. Here are some sample main ideas:

Shopping is much easier in the US than in my home country.

The stores in the US are different from the stores in my home country.

I enjoyed grocery shopping in my home country, but I don't enjoy it here.

Looking at Your Goals   Think back on your goals for this unit.

How well can you . . .	Not very well		Somewhat		Very well
describe items that you want to return?	1	2	3	4	5
understand catalog descriptions?	1	2	3	4	5
interpret newspaper ads?	1	2	3	4	5
ask for information about products?	1	2	3	4	5
describe items that you want to sell?	1	2	3	4	5
another goal:_____	1	2	3	4	5

Learning about Different Ways to Shop   Think back on the lessons.

What was the most important thing you learned about different ways to shop?

_____

_____

What do you still need to learn about different ways to shop? List one or two things.

_____

_____

Improving Your English   In this unit you studied these things. Check the ones that have improved.

_____ using shopping words

_____ using superlative adjectives

_____ using *used to*

_____ pronouncing reduced *to*

_____ comparing information in catalog descriptions

_____ stressing superlative adjectives

_____ listening for details in radio ads

_____ scanning for information in classified ads

_____ _____
another thing that you improved

Lesson 1 Laying Down the Law

Exercise A   Read the story. Then answer the questions in complete sentences. Use the underlined words in your answers.

John was 16 years old. He had a good family that cared about him. His parents told him about the danger of using drugs and alcohol. John knew that it was against the law for him to drink alcohol at his friend's party. But his friends told him that it was OK. So he drank beer all night. His friend offered him some marijuana, too. He started smoking it as he walked outside. On his way out the door, a policeman stopped him. He took John and two other teenagers to the police station. John's parents had to pay $300, and he had to spend two months in a home for teenagers. While he was at the home, he couldn't make phone calls after 6 P.M. He really missed his family and his freedom.

1. What was the <u>illegal substance</u> in the story?

     _____

2. What did the policeman <u>arrest</u> John for?

     _____

3. How much was the <u>fine</u>?

     _____

4. What was John's <u>sentence</u>?

     _____

5. What was <u>prohibited</u> at the home for teenagers?

     _____

Exercise B Read the article about the US Food and Drug Administration.

The Food and Drug Administration

There are three kinds of drugs in US law: *over-the-counter* drugs, which people can buy without a prescription; *prescription* drugs, which a doctor must prescribe; and *controlled substances,* which are drugs that people may abuse. Most controlled substances are prescription drugs, but some are illegal drugs.

The Food and Drug Administration (FDA) is a government agency that inspects drugs and other products for safety. It decides which drugs are prescription and which are over-the-counter. The FDA requires labels on prescription drugs. The label means that it is illegal to give the drug to anyone that it isn't prescribed for. The label may look like this:

> **Caution:** Federal law prohibits the transfer of this drug to any person other than the patient for whom it was prescribed.

Another label means that people might become addicted to the drug. It looks like this:

> **Warning:** May be habit-forming.

If a product has a label like this, the FDA has not inspected it:

> This statement has not been evaluated by the Food and Drug Administration.

The label means that the scientists at the FDA did not inspect the product, and they don't know if the product can really do what the package says it can do.

The FDA also has programs to reduce tobacco use. Tobacco laws are different in different states, but smoking is now prohibited in many public places all over the US. As you can see from the line graph, however, the number of new tobacco users remains high. Some people would like the FDA to make tobacco a controlled substance, so that it would be more difficult to buy cigarettes and start smoking. Many people disagree with that idea.

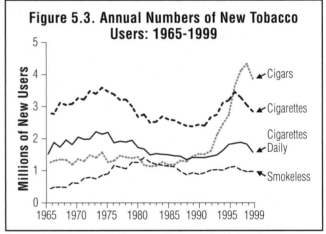

Figure 5.3. Annual Numbers of New Tobacco Users: 1965-1999

Source: U.S. Substance Abuse and Mental Health Services Administration (SAMHSA), Office of Applied Studies, *National Household Survey on Drug Abuse* 1999–2001

Answer these questions in your notebook. Write complete sentences.

1. Describe three things that the FDA does.

2. Look at the graph. Which year had the lowest number of new daily smokers? Which had the highest number?

Lesson 2 Protecting Children

Exercise A Match the opinions with the examples.

___e___ **1.** Sometimes getting angry can teach a child a lesson.

_____ **2.** Permitting children to use the Internet alone can be dangerous.

_____ **3.** If you hit children when you are angry, you might hurt them.

_____ **4.** Grounding your teenager is a good way to discipline.

_____ **5.** Neglecting your children's needs can cause emotional harm.

_____ **6.** Children have trouble learning at schools that allow corporal punishment.

a. After my 16-year-old had to stay home all weekend, he changed his behavior.

b. My teacher used to hit students on the hand with a ruler. We were afraid of her!

c. I know a boy who slapped his father. The father was so upset that he beat the boy.

d. A 14-year-old girl was killed by a man she met online.

e. When my little girl ran into the street, I pulled her back and yelled at her. After that, she remembered!

f. If a mother rarely pays attention to her children, they may be unhappy.

Write the opinions and their matching examples on the lines below. Connect the two ideas with "For example."

1. _Sometimes getting angry can teach a child a lesson. For example, when my little girl ran_
into the street, I pulled her back and yelled at her. After that, she remembered!

2. _____

_____

3. _____

_____

4. _____

_____

5. _____

_____

6. _____

_____

Exercise B Use these words to fill in the blanks.

abusive	alcoholic	get involved

Most people understand that if someone is hurting a child, they need to call the police or Child Protective Services. But what do you do if an adult is being hurt? Should you _____ ? If a woman you know often has bruises and cuts and you suspect that
1
her husband is _____ , do you say anything? What if your friend's wife drinks
2
too much? Do you make a suggestion about how an _____ can get help?
3

Write an answer to these questions in your notebook.

Exercise C In your notebook, write a story about someone who was good at disciplining children. Think about your own experience as a child, your experience as a parent, people you have known, and stories you have read in the newspaper. You can write about yourself, a teacher, a parent, or another person. Use the chart to prepare for writing.

Who the story is about

↓

What the child did

↓

What the adult did

↓

The result

↓

My opinion

Lesson 3 A Helping Hand

Exercise A A mother is speaking to a hotline operator about her teenage son. Use these words to fill in the blanks. Use each word only once.

aggressive	depression	enthusiastic	lethargic
appetite	enthusiasm	irrational	reckless

Operator: Is your son very tired and lazy?

Caller: Yes, he has been very _____
                1
for a few months.

Operator: Does he eat a normal amount of food?

Caller: No. He hasn't had an _____
                2
for two weeks.

Operator: Is he involved in any activities that he gets

excited about?

Caller: He used to love playing tennis. He was very _____ about
                    3
trying to get on the team. But now he's not interested. He hasn't had any

_____ for anything lately.
        4

Operator: Is he usually friendly?

Caller: Well, normally he is friendly. But lately he has been very mean and

_____ .
        5

Operator: All of these could be signs of _____ . Is there any other behavior
                        6
you can tell me about?

Caller: Yes. We had to take the car away because his driving was fast and

_____ . And he often says very strange, _____
        7   8
things that I don't understand.

Operator: It sounds like your son may be depressed or he may have a substance abuse

problem. Why don't you make an appointment with one of our counselors? If you

bring your son into the clinic, you can both talk to the counselor.

Exercise B   Read the story. Circle the correct words.

Leticia went to the treatment center to talk about her neighbor.

When the counselor asked her about the problem, she said, "I

| **1.** hear   heard   have heard | the mother yelling and screaming many

times in the past. One time I | **2.** seen   have seen   saw | her slap her

daughter in the face. I'm pretty sure she was drunk. I

| **3.** smelled   smell   have smelled | alcohol on her several times."

The counselor said, "Have you | **4.** speak   spoke   spoken | to

the mother?"

Leticia said, "No, I've never | **5.** had   have   has | a real conversation

with her. One time last month I | **6.** have asked   ask   asked | her how

old her daughter was. But she wasn't very friendly. I

| **7.** have tried   trying   try | to talk to her a couple of times this month,

but she never seems interested in talking to me."

The counselor said, "Have you | **8.** met   meet   meeting |

her daughter?"

Leticia said, "Yes, last week she was playing outside my apartment,

and I | **9.** have started   start   started | to talk to her. But her

mother heard us, and | **10.** has told   have told   told | her to come

inside. She hasn't played outside for a week. I don't think she

| **11.** has gone   goes   going | to school this week, either."

The counselor said, "I think that you should call Child Protective

Services. It sounds like a serious problem for the child. If the child's

mother is ever friendlier to you, please give her my card."

Looking at Your Goals   Think back on your goals for this unit.

How well can you . . .	Not very well		Somewhat		Very well
describe symptoms of drug abuse?	1	2	3	4	5
explain your ideas about disciplining children?	1	2	3	4	5
understand laws about child abuse?	1	2	3	4	5
write an argument about drug or alcohol laws?	1	2	3	4	5
make a telephone call to a government agency?	1	2	3	4	5
another goal:_____	1	2	3	4	5

Learning about Drug and Child Abuse Laws   Think back on the lessons.

What was the most important thing you learned about drug and child abuse laws?

_____

_____

What do you still need to learn about these laws? List one or two things.

_____

_____

Improving Your English   In this unit you studied these things. Check the ones that have improved.

_____ using words about abuse and support

_____ using gerunds as subjects and objects

_____ pronouncing reduced -ing

_____ using the present perfect

_____ dropping initial h after consonant sounds

_____ scanning for information in a memo

_____ reading and applying information about laws

_____ listening for main ideas in a television ad

_____ writing a convincing argument

_____ _____
<small>another thing that you improved</small>

Lesson 1   Get the Ball Rolling

Exercise A   Read the story about Marlene. Answer the questions with complete sentences. Use the underlined words in your answers. One question has been answered as an example.

Volunteering

Marlene has always liked working with other people on projects. But when she was younger, she didn't have much time. She was a single mother, and she was very busy raising her daughter.

After Jenny moved out of the house, Marlene had more free time. She thought about helping out at her grandson's school. She called the teacher to see if she could work in the classroom. The teacher thanked Marlene for offering to help, but she didn't need help in the class. She told Marlene to call someone on the school carnival committee. The president of the committee was very happy that Marlene wanted to work on the committee. She asked for Marlene's help with the decorations. Marlene said that she'd be happy to help. She told the committee president that she thought it would be a good idea to buy balloons and make posters.

Everybody on the committee worked hard, and the carnival was a big success. Since then, Marlene has gotten involved in many more community projects and events.

1. What did Marlene <u>consider</u> doing?

   She considered helping out at her grandson's school.

2. What did Marlene <u>volunteer</u> to do?

   _____

3. What did the teacher <u>appreciate</u>?

   _____

4. What did the teacher <u>recommend</u>?

   _____

5. What did the president of the committee <u>request</u>?

   _____

6. Did Marlene <u>mind</u> helping with the decorations?

   _____

Exercise B Answer the questions to write about yourself. Use the underlined word.

1. What do you <u>enjoy</u> doing?

_____

2. What do you <u>miss</u> doing?

_____

3. What do you usually <u>avoid</u> doing?

_____

Exercise C When Jenny went to City Hall to ask for permission to clean up the park, a clerk gave her this flyer.

Keep Our City Beautiful
THE NEIGHBORHOOD CLEANUP PROGRAM

The Neighborhood Cleanup program is available for groups that want to beautify their neighborhoods. If you want to paint over graffiti or remove trash, the city will provide paint, brushes, brooms, rakes, gloves, trash bags, and a large dumpster. You must return any supplies that can be used again for another cleanup project. Any community organization, Neighborhood Watch group, or volunteer group is eligible to apply for the program. You must apply at least two weeks in advance. Just call the Neighborhood Services Department at (616) 555-6735 and tell us what project your volunteer group wants to do. We will give you a "Request for Assistance" form to complete and return. The form must include the name and address of each person who will participate in the cleanup.

This program cannot be used to clean up one person's private property. However, 15 households can join together to use the program for property cleanup. Do not use the city dumpster for tires, batteries, flammable materials, paint, motor oil, or other dangerous materials. Hundreds of neighborhood groups have used this program to make our city beautiful. Thank you for pitching in!

For more information, call us at (616) 555-6735.

---

rake

dumpster

What will Jenny and Marlene do next? Use the information from the flyer to describe how they will organize the cleanup. Write a paragraph in your notebook. You could start like this:

First, they will call the Neighborhood Services Department. Then, . . .

Lesson 2 Sign on the Dotted Line

Exercise A   Read the story. Write the correct words on the lines.

Jenny was an only child. Her parents got divorced when she was 10 years old. Her father

_____ to a different city. Jenny was a good student, and after high school,
1. moves / has moved / moved

she _____ to college for four years. But she _____ her
2. goes / went / has gone away   3. misses / has missed / missed

mother and the friends she grew up with, so she moved back to her hometown after college.

Soon, she _____ a man at a friend's party. A year later, they got married.
4. meets / met / has met

Now she lives only a few miles from the house she grew up in, and she _____
5. visits / visited / has visited

her mother often. She _____ since her children were born, but sometimes
6. doesn't work / hasn't worked /
didn't work

she _____ her mother with community projects. She feels that she
7. helps / has helped / helped

_____ a lot in the past few years, and now she's ready to look for a job.
8. has learned / learns / learned

Exercise B   Use these words to fill in the blanks. Use the correct form of
each word.

approval	approve	influence	issue	oppose	petition	representative

A few years ago, Jenny noticed that students were buying junk food at her son's school. She

talked to other parents about the _____ . She learned that most people did not
1

like children getting junk food before lunch, and many were _____ to any
2

junk food at school. She decided to write a _____ and present it to the principal.
3

The principal agreed with the parents, so he _____ their idea to stop selling junk
4

food. But the principal couldn't make the decision by himself. He had to ask the school board for

their _____ of decisions that would cost the school money. He told Jenny that
5

the parents should choose a _____ to speak for them at the school board
6

meeting. One of the parents who signed the petition was a doctor. Jenny wanted him to attend the

meeting because she thought his arguments might _____ the board's decision.
7

Exercise C In your notebook, write about things that you have done. Then write about when you did them. Choose from the following ideas.

- cook for a large group
- teach someone to drive
- sleep outside

- stay awake all night
- fall down
- eat a big meal

- watch a parade
- go to a carnival
- speak to a school administrator

I have cooked for very large groups. Last month, I cooked for my parents' anniversary party.

Exercise D Marlene wrote her petition because the new hospital caused a parking problem in her neighborhood. Her idea for a solution was to give out permits to residents and limit parking for other people to two hours. Think about your community. What would you like to change? It could be a problem that you see, or a service that is not offered. Look at the example of a problem/solution map. Think of a third solution and write your ideas in the center box. Then in your notebook make a problem/solution map with a problem you would like to solve and two ways to solve it.

speed bump

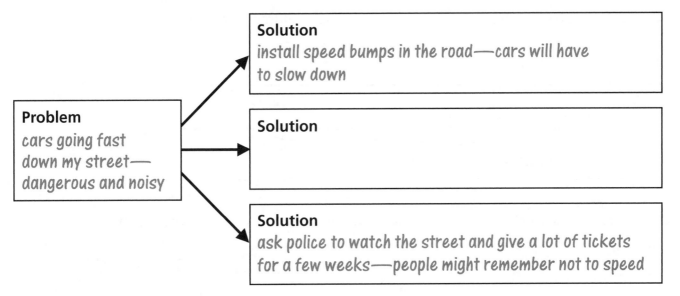

Problem
cars going fast down my street—dangerous and noisy

Solution
install speed bumps in the road—cars will have to slow down

Solution

Solution
ask police to watch the street and give a lot of tickets for a few weeks—people might remember not to speed

Use the ideas in your problem/solution map to write a letter in your notebook to the city or to the police. Explain the problem and how you think it can be solved.

Check your writing:

- Did you put a comma after *Dear _____* and *Sincerely?*
- Did you indent the first sentence?
- Look for present perfect verbs and verbs followed by gerunds. Did you use them correctly?

Lesson 3 Actions Speak Louder Than Words

Exercise A Write a sentence about yourself with each word or phrase. One sentence has been written as an example.

1. (donate) _I have donated time putting up flowers at church._

2. (donate) _____

3. (improve) _____

4. (team player) _____

Exercise B Fill in the blanks with *for* or *since*.

1. Marlene has been divorced _____ 30 years.

2. She has lived in the same neighborhood _____ 40 years.

3. She has been a grandmother _____ 1990.

4. Jenny has sent out three resumes _____ July.

5. She hasn't had a job _____ her children were born.

Look at the time line about Marlene.

2000	Now	time line
	volunteered at fund-raisers	

Write one sentence with *for* and one sentence with *since* about Marlene's volunteer work.

6. _____

_____

7. _____

_____

One Step Up
Make a time line about one or more things you have done. Write sentences about your time line.

Exercise C Read the story about Jenny. Fill in the blanks with the simple past or present perfect form of the verb.

1. Jenny _____ a mother for 13 years. Her first son _____
   _{be}   _{be}
   born in 1990.

2. She _____ a secretary before her son was born. She _____
   _{be}   _{have}
   several different jobs.

3. She _____ with the school carnival for the past three years. Last
   _{help}
   year, she _____ several of the food booths.
   _{arrange}

4. She and Marlene _____ many family activities together. Two years
   _{do}
   ago, they _____ a big family reunion.
   _{plan}

5. Jenny _____ to another country. But last year, she and her
   _{travel, never}
   family _____ to Hawaii.
   _{go}

6. She _____ to work on houses. Last summer she
   _{love, always}
   _____ a lot of flowers. They look beautiful now.
   _{plant}

7. She _____ her children to the museum many times. In fact, she
   _{take}
   _____ them last weekend.
   _{take}

Exercise D Use these words to fill in the blanks.

block party	carnival	committee	fund-raiser	mural	parade

1. You can decorate a wall in your neighborhood with a _____ .

2. A group of people who work together is called a _____ .

3. When you sell candy for the school, it's called a _____ .

4. Children play games and win prizes at a _____ .

5. Organizations march down the street during a _____ .

6. A _____ is a good event for neighbors to get to know each other.

Looking at Your Goals   Think back on your goals for this unit.

How well can you . . .	Not very well		Somewhat		Very well
ask for help with a project?	1	2	3	4	5
speak up at a meeting?	1	2	3	4	5
write a petition to change something?	1	2	3	4	5
plan a project and describe it in detail?	1	2	3	4	5
describe personal qualities to use on a resume?	1	2	3	4	5
another goal:_____	1	2	3	4	5

Learning about Getting Involved with Your Community
Think back on the lessons.

What was the most important thing you learned about getting involved with your community?

_____

_____

What do you still need to learn about how to get involved with your community? List one or two things.

_____

_____

Improving Your English   In this unit you studied these things. Check the ones that have improved.

_____ using community involvement words

_____ using verbs followed by gerunds

_____ using present perfect with *for* and *since*

_____ pronouncing diphthongs

_____ placing stress on adjectives

_____ listening for details in a conversation

_____ reading for the general idea in a petition

_____ identifying important information when reading a resume

_____ _____
another thing that you improved

Lesson 1 Study Habits

Exercise A   Use *will* or *be going to* to complete the answers below.

1. What are your plans for this weekend?

I _____ some time at the library.
<u>spend</u>

2. I don't understand these instructions.

Don't worry. I _____ you with them.
<u>help</u>

3. Why can't you come to the party tomorrow?

I _____ my sister tomorrow night.
<u>visit</u>

4. Why is Tom coming over?

He _____ the sink for us.
<u>fix</u>

5. I can't get this jar open!

I _____ it for you.
<u>do</u>

6. What do you want to do when you graduate?

I _____ a pharmacist.
<u>be</u>

Exercise B   Match the sentences in the first column with similar sentences in the second column.

_____ **1.** You're <u>distracting</u> me.   a. You don't study regularly.

_____ **2.** You're <u>making excuses</u>.   b. You have to sign up for your classes.

_____ **3.** You're <u>inconsistent</u> about studying.   c. You're bothering me.

_____ **4.** You need to make studying a <u>priority</u>.   d. Your reasons are poor.

_____ **5.** You need to <u>register</u>.   e. Studying should be important to you.

Exercise C   The pie chart shows how Anthony spends his time. He needs to make time for studying. In the circle on the right, make a pie chart that shows how Anthony can change his schedule.

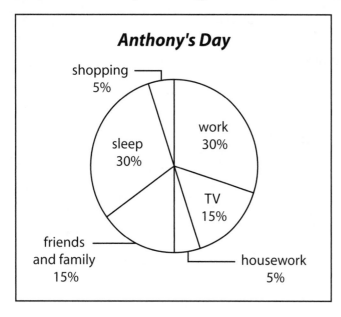

Anthony's Day

shopping 5%
work 30%
sleep 30%
TV 15%
friends and family 15%
housework 5%

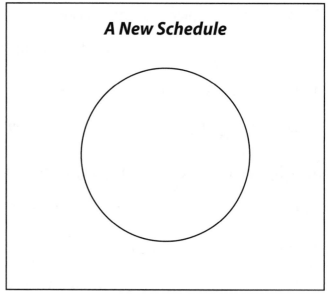

A New Schedule

In-Class Extension   Make a pie chart in your notebook showing how you spend your time. Share it with your group.

Exercise D   Use the vocabulary words and idioms to write sentences about yourself. One sentence has been written as an example.

1. (priority) _My schedule is very busy, but studying English is a priority for me._

2. (consistent) _____

3. (inconsistent) _____

4. (routine) _____

5. (schedule) _____

6. (distract) _____

7. (distraction) _____

8. (priority) _____

9. (fall behind) _____

10. (catch up) _____

11. (make excuses) _____

Lesson 2 Get Informed

Exercise A Match the correct section of the library or bookstore to the book title.

_____ 1. Biography

_____ 2. Self-Help

_____ 3. Health

_____ 4. Science

_____ 5. History

_____ 6. Reference

_____ 7. Sports

_____ 8. Personal Finance

_____ 9. Travel

_____ 10. Fiction

a. *How to Get the Most for Your Money*

b. *The American Heritage Dictionary*

c. *Thailand in Ten Days*

d. *How to Control Your Anger*

e. *The Mystery of the Missing Diamonds*

f. *The Life of Henry Ford*

g. *The Truth about Vitamins*

h. *The United States in the Gulf War*

i. *All about Space*

j. *A Short History of Baseball*

Exercise B Use these words to fill in the blanks.

| advantage | documentary | look up | opportunity | reference | research |

After Anthony talked to Cameron's pediatrician, he decided to go to the library to learn more about ADHD. First, he went to the

_____ desk because he knew the librarian there could
              1

help him get started on his _____ . She showed him how
                                          2

to _____ the names of books and articles on the
        3

computer. If he wanted to watch a _____ about ADHD, he could check the
                                                4

video section. The library also had plenty of computers with access to the Internet. The

librarian offered to help him with an online search about his topic. He decided to take

_____ of this _____ to learn more about ADHD.
        5   6

Exercise C In your notebook, write a polite question to ask a librarian with each of these words. Use *where, when, what,* or *how* in your questions. One question has been written as an example.

article	biographies	due	nonfiction	periodical	research

Could you please show me how I can research ADHD?

Exercise D Many libraries have a web site where you can get information about the library services. Read the FAQ (frequently asked questions) page from one library web site. The answers to these questions may be different at your library.

frequently = often

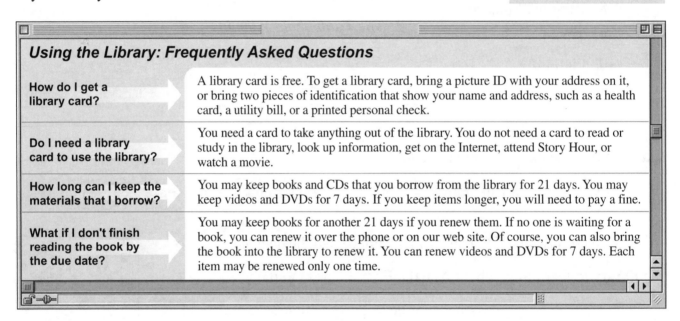

Using the Library: Frequently Asked Questions

How do I get a library card?	A library card is free. To get a library card, bring a picture ID with your address on it, or bring two pieces of identification that show your name and address, such as a health card, a utility bill, or a printed personal check.
Do I need a library card to use the library?	You need a card to take anything out of the library. You do not need a card to read or study in the library, look up information, get on the Internet, attend Story Hour, or watch a movie.
How long can I keep the materials that I borrow?	You may keep books and CDs that you borrow from the library for 21 days. You may keep videos and DVDs for 7 days. If you keep items longer, you will need to pay a fine.
What if I don't finish reading the book by the due date?	You may keep books for another 21 days if you renew them. If no one is waiting for a book, you can renew it over the phone or on our web site. Of course, you can also bring the book into the library to renew it. You can renew videos and DVDs for 7 days. Each item may be renewed only one time.

Choose the correct word or phrase to complete each sentence. Write the letter of your choice on the line.

_____ **1.** A library book is _____ after 21 days.
   a. lost   c. on time
   b. overdue   d. borrowed

_____ **2.** You can _____ a library book one time.
   a. check out   c. renew
   b. borrow   d. read

_____ **3.** You need a library card to _____ .
   a. get on the Internet   c. attend Story Hour
   b. watch a movie   d. check out a book

Lesson 3 Back to School

Exercise A Fill in the blanks. Use each word or phrase only once.

admissions	earn	fees	requirements
drop	enroll	never too late	tuition

Two years ago, I went to school to study electronics, but my mother became ill, and I had to _____ my classes to take care of her. I went to the _____
1   2
office to tell them. They gave me a refund on the tuition. Later I changed my mind about what to study. I'm going to _____ in college next month. I plan to
3
_____ a degree in nursing. One of the _____ for the degree
4   5
is to complete the science classes with a grade of *B* or better. It's expensive, but I've been saving money. I hope I can afford the _____ and _____. It
6   7
might take me 10 years, but I believe that it's _____ to learn.
8

Exercise B Find the words below in the puzzle. Words may be written forwards or backwards, across, down or diagonally. After you circle each word, write a sentence with it in your notebook.

add	career	fulfilling	practical	resource
advantage	enrollment	meaningful	register	

```
b  m  e  a  n  i  n  g  f  u  l  l  u  j  k  j  a  e  e  f  g  c
e  a  o  e  a  s  e  r  d  m  b  i  l  v  r  a  c  b  n  n  w  a
p  n  d  c  q  h  o  r  e  s  o  u  r  c  e  p  y  b  r  b  h  r
u  r  t  v  d  u  m  y  o  s  t  b  k  n  g  o  l  r  o  s  i  e
b  e  a  v  a  g  e  f  u  l  f  i  l  l  i  n  g  n  l  x  s  e
c  c  t  c  u  n  l  m  h  n  j  k  u  o  s  o  p  k  l  k  p  r
m  n  c  u  t  w  t  r  v  a  u  y  e  w  t  g  c  x  m  p  e  y
o  o  e  i  u  i  h  a  f  e  d  e  r  p  e  y  i  n  e  b  r  f
h  c  p  t  r  e  c  i  g  r  d  d  m  n  r  f  d  s  n  w  i  u
k  i  x  t  r  e  w  a  s  e  r  e  s  o  l  u  t  i  t  n  l  u
n  b  e  d  f  e  r  t  l  t  i  o  k  j  t  r  e  h  b  k  l  o
```

Exercise C Change the direct questions to polite questions. The first one is done as an example.

1. Where is the community college?

   Could you tell me where the community college is? _____?

2. What days does the class meet?

   Do you know _____?

3. When does registration begin?

   Could you tell me _____?

4. When is children's story hour?

   Do you know _____?

Exercise D Think about your education. Choose one of the following levels of education and write it in the center circle of an idea map like the one below.

- Elementary Education (ages 5–12)
- Secondary Education (ages 13–18)
- Adult School
- College

In the other circles, write about things that you remember.

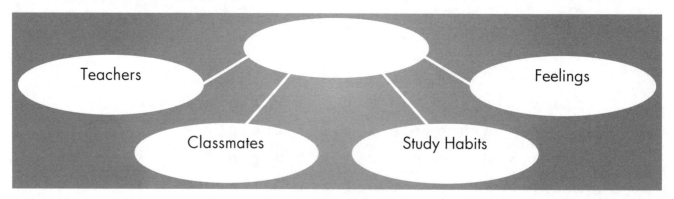

Write a paragraph in your notebook. First write a main-idea sentence. Use ideas from your chart to support the main idea. Here are some possible main-idea sentences:

   I have many happy memories about elementary school.

   High school was very difficult for me.

   My study habits have changed a lot since high school.

Looking at Your Goals Think back on your goals for this unit.

How well can you . . .	Not very well		Somewhat		Very well
talk about future plans?	1	2	3	4	5
understand good study habits?	1	2	3	4	5
use library resources?	1	2	3	4	5
ask politely for information or help?	1	2	3	4	5
understand recorded enrollment procedures?	1	2	3	4	5
another goal: _____	1	2	3	4	5

Learning about Becoming a Lifelong Learner Think back on the lessons.

What was the most important thing you learned about becoming a lifelong learner?

_____

_____

What do you still need to learn about becoming a lifelong learner?
List one or two things.

_____

_____

Improving Your English In this unit you studied these things. Check the ones that have improved.

_____ understanding words for learning and planning

_____ using *will* and *be going to* for the future tense

_____ pronouncing reduced *be* and *will*

_____ pronouncing reduced *would you* and *could you*

_____ making polite requests with modals

_____ drawing conclusions from an article

_____ finding information in a library catalog

_____ listening for specific information in a phone recording

_____ _____
another thing that you improved

Lesson 1 Go with the Flow

Exercise A   Read the paragraph. Answer the questions in complete sentences. Use the present perfect progressive in your answers. The first question has been answered as an example.

> Rania has been thinking about starting her own business. For two months, she has been researching how to start an Internet business selling children's clothes. She has also been drawing pictures of clothes that she would like to make. Because she's been spending so much time at work, she doesn't think she'll be able to start her own business for about a year.

1. What has Rania been thinking about doing?

She has been thinking about starting her own business.

2. How long has Rania been researching her new business?

_____

3. What kind of business has Rania been researching?

_____

4. Why won't Rania be able to start her business right away?

_____

Exercise B   Match the sentences in the first column with the sentences in the second column.

_____ **1.** She has been out in the rain.   a. She wants to get a better job.

_____ **2.** She has been working all night.   b. She's going to have a party.

_____ **3.** She has been studying English.   c. A lot of new businesses have moved in.

_____ **4.** She has been calling her friends.   d. Her clothes are wet.

_____ **5.** Her neighborhood has been   e. She's tired.
            changing lately.

In your notebook, write new pairs of sentences. Use the present perfect progressive in the first sentence.

Exercise C Unscramble these sentences. Make sentences about Rania's job and write them on the lines below. Add correct punctuation. Use a capital letter where necessary.

1. update / Rania's / boss / to / equipment / the / wanted

   _____

2. the / way / co-workers / same / her / reacted

   _____

3. said / but / you / adapt / will / her / boss

   _____

4. he / new / a / production / will / effect / positive / on / have / machines / said

   _____

5. they / forward / looking / the / training / weren't / mandatory / to

   _____

6. a / workshop / announced / he

   _____

7. Rania's / very / wasn't / positive / reaction

   _____

8. with / always / employees / but / to / deal / change / have

   _____

9. it / for / resisted / long / time / they / a

   _____

In-Class Extension With your group, decide on a logical order for these sentences. Write them in paragraph form. Trade your paragraph with another group. Check the order of their sentences and their punctuation.

Lesson 2 Learn New Technology

Exercise A Read the letter that Rania's friend sent to her. Use these words to fill in the blanks.

| bar codes | laying off | network | scanning | touch-screen |

Dear Rania,

Sorry I haven't written for so long. I have been working for a large retail company, but I'm afraid I won't have my job much longer. They have been _____ a lot of

1
people lately. They spent a lot of money on updating equipment in their stores. All the office

computers are connected to one _____ . Every cashier has brand-new

2

_____ machines that read the prices quickly. The machines are small and

3

cordless, so cashiers can scan the _____ on any item. The company also

4

installed a _____ catalog where customers can order products just by

5

touching the pictures of the items. The company has spent so much money on all of this

technology that now they are having problems. I'm very worried about my future here.

Love,
Tarah

Exercise B Fill in the blank in each sentence about technological change. Write the verbs in present perfect continuous or present perfect form. In some sentences, either verb form is correct.

1. That store _____ scanning equipment for many years. They have a

use
   machine at every checkout stand.

2. The employees _____ new bar codes on all of the items because the

put
   prices have changed.

3. Computers _____ touch screens for many years.

have

4. The display on the clock radio _____ clear for three days.

be, not

5. That company _____ a lot of employees lately.

lay off

6. Some people _____ with the changes very well.

cope, not

Exercise C Read the paragraphs and answer the questions below.

Overcoming Fear and Confronting Challenges

Everyone knows how good it feels to succeed or do well at something. But what happens when you don't pass a test, meet an important goal, or get that job you interviewed for? When people fail to do what they are expected to do, they are usually disappointed. Sometimes people feel that no matter how hard they try, they can't succeed. It's easy to give up.

We all make mistakes because we're human. We need to learn from those mistakes and failures so that we can improve the next time. If we try to succeed at something and we make mistakes, we need to forgive ourselves. If we fail, we need to try again.

Challenges are a part of life. Completing high school and college, finding and keeping good jobs, getting married, staying married, and raising a family are just a few of many challenges in life. All of these challenges create opportunities for success or failure. When we confront our challenges instead of running from them, we have already succeeded. Overcoming our fear of failure is important. Difficult situations can teach us many things if we look at them as opportunities for growth.

1. What is the main idea of this reading?

_____

2. Do you agree? Explain your answer.

_____

Exercise D In your notebook, write a paragraph about something you have done that was difficult or challenging. Tell what you learned from it. Use the chart to prepare for writing.

What was the challenge?	
How did you cope with it?	
Were you able to overcome your fears?	

Lesson 3 Three Cheers!

Exercise A   Write the first part of each sentence. Begin with *If*.

1. _____ , I'll never speak to you again.

2. _____ , you'll have to start over.

3. _____ , she'll look for a new job.

Write the second part of the sentence. Use the words *will* or *won't*.

4. If I confront my fears, _____ .

5. If you overcome your shyness, _____ .

6. If you weigh the pros and cons, _____ .

Exercise B   Read the story. Circle the correct words.

When I got my new digital watch, I couldn't figure out how to
program it. I | **1.** want   wanted   have wanted | to set the date, but the
display was very confusing. I accidentally set the alarm, and the watch
wouldn't stop | **2.** beeping   to beep   beep | . I took it back to the store.
The clerk | **3.** helps   helped   was helping | another customer, and he
didn't notice me. I was embarrassed because the watch kept
| **4.** beeping   beeped   to beep | . People | **5.** stare   are staring
were staring | at me. Finally, another clerk helped me. She
| **6.** tried   has tried   tries | to fix the watch, but she couldn't. She said,
"If you come back tomorrow, the manager | **7.** is   will be   has been |
here. He | **8.** is knowing   know   knows | how to program these
watches." I said, "I | **9.** have been trying   am trying   try | to set this
watch all day! I | **10.** don't ever have   have never have   have never had |
so much trouble with a watch before. Could you please just give me a
refund?" She | **11.** was giving   gave   has given | me the refund. I
| **12.** haven't been buying   haven't bought   don't buy | a new watch yet,
but next time, I | **13.** buy   buying   am going to buy | a simple watch.

Exercise C Use the words in the box on the right to fill in the crossword puzzle. Be sure your answer fits in the puzzle before you go on to the next sentence.

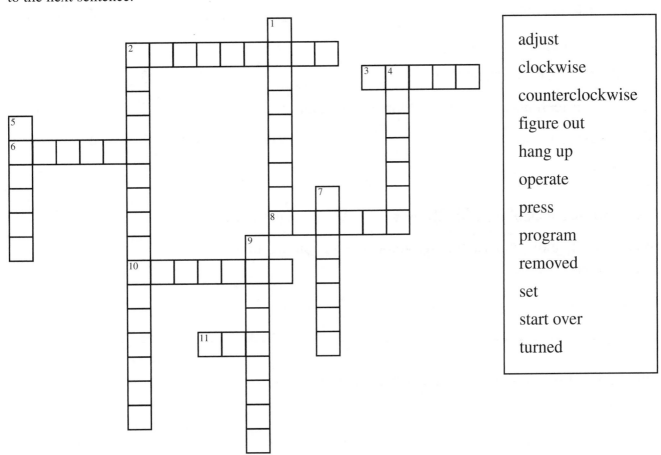

adjust

clockwise

counterclockwise

figure out

hang up

operate

press

program

removed

set

start over

turned

Across

2. Turn the oven dial _____ to turn on the heat.

3. _____ the red button to turn the machine on.

6. You can _____ the ringing to loud, medium, or soft.

8. When I _____ the dial, it broke off.

10. I learned how to _____ some new equipment.

11. Every spring and fall we have to _____ our watches to a new time.

Down

1. I read the instructions three times, but I couldn't _____ how to build the bookcase.

2. Turn the volume dial _____ to turn off the sound.

4. He _____ the old printer cartridge and put in a new one.

5. You have to _____ before you can listen to your phone messages.

7. I use a computer _____ to make birthday cards.

9. If you make a mistake, you need to stop and _____ .

Looking at Your Goals   Think back on your goals for this unit.

How well can you . . .	Not very well		Somewhat		Very well
discuss pros and cons?	1	2	3	4	5
explain how to use something?	1	2	3	4	5
describe the effects of technology?	1	2	3	4	5
discuss your feelings about different kinds of changes?	1	2	3	4	5
give a presentation?	1	2	3	4	5
another goal: _____	1	2	3	4	5

Learning about Dealing with Change   Think back on the lessons.

What was the most important thing you learned about dealing
with change?

_____

_____

What do you still need to learn about dealing with change?
List one or two things.

_____

_____

Improving Your English   In this unit you studied these things. Check the
ones that have improved.

_____ understanding words about dealing
with change

_____ using present perfect continuous

_____ using primary and secondary stress

_____ using present and future sentences
with *if*

_____ using list intonation

_____ focusing on important ideas in a memo

_____ interpreting graphs

_____ listening for main ideas in
a conversation

_____ _____
another thing that you improved

Vocabulary

These are the words you learned in this unit.

- aerobics
- ceramics
- challenge
- challenging
- cheerleading
- chess
- compete
- competitive
- confidence
- confident
- conflict
- crafts
- disrespectful
- fitness
- flexible
- fulfill
- generation
- gymnastics
- individual
- inflexible
- irresponsible
- join
- lectures
- martial arts
- opportunity
- participate
- reliable
- respectful
- responsible
- risky
- team
- unreliable

Grammar Talk: Simple Present Questions and Statements

Is the Senior Center open on Sundays?	The Senior Center **isn't** open on Sundays.
Does the Senior Center **offer** aerobics?	The Senior Center **offers** aerobics.
When **does** the Senior Center **open**?	The Senior Center **opens** at 7:30 A.M.
Where **do** we **go** for lectures?	We **go** to room 23 for lectures.

Which questions have do *or* does? *Why? Which statements have verbs that end in* s? *Why do they end in* s?

Grammar Talk: Agreement and Disagreement

June thinks that coming to work late is irresponsible, **and I do too.**

June thinks that many people are unreliable, **and so do I.**

June doesn't think that younger people are more flexible, **and neither do I.**

June doesn't think that most young people are reliable, **and I don't either.**

June thinks that older workers are more responsible, **but I don't.**

June doesn't think that young workers learn more quickly, **but I do.**

In the first sentence, what does too *mean? What is the difference between* neither *and* either? *How are the last two sentences different?*

Grammar Talk: Statements with Past Continuous and Simple Past

Jae Lee **was bowing** to his Tae Kwon Do teacher.
He **fell** over.

Sarah **was slouching** in her chair.
Her father **told** her to sit up straight.

Sam and Koji **were staring** at the pretty girl.
She **walked** away from them.

Which actions were continuous? Which actions interrupted the other ones?

Grammar Talk: Direct Speech

Jae Lee said, **"I**'m sorry that your clothes aren't ready. Please excuse the misunderstanding.**"**

Valerie said, **"P**lease forgive me for being late. I was talking to an important customer.**"**

These sentences show exactly what the people said. Where is the comma in each sentence? Where are the quotation marks? Notice that each quote begins with a capital letter.

Vocabulary

These are the words you learned in this unit.

- aggressive
- apologize
- apology
- body language
- bow
- concerned
- excuse me
- expect
- expectation
- fault
- forgive me
- gesture
- impatient
- impolite
- interrupt
- misunderstand
- misunderstanding
- mix-up
- nudge
- offend
- offensive
- pardon me
- polite
- resolution
- resolve
- rude
- shrug
- slouch
- snap your fingers
- stare
- whisper
- whistle
- wink

Vocabulary

These are the words you learned in this unit.

- bruise
- cause
- escape route
- fire extinguisher
- fracture
- injure
- injury
- knock over
- lock up
- mugged
- plug in
- poison
- poisonous
- prevent
- prevention
- put away
- replace
- rob
- robbery
- shock
- slip
- slippery
- smash
- smoke detector
- spill
- sprain
- stolen
- stranger
- suspect
- suspicious
- treat
- trip over
- unplug
- victim
- witness
- wound

Grammar Talk: Past-Tense Questions and Answers

Where **did** Miguel **knock over** the oil?
He **knocked** it **over** near the grill.

When **did** you **smash** your fingers?
I **smashed** them yesterday.

Where **were** you when it happened?
I **was** at the factory.

What is the main verb in each question? Is did *used in past-tense questions with the verb* be?

Grammar Talk: Sentences with *when, before,* and *after*

when	I was scared **when** the smoke detector went off. **When** the smoke detector went off, I was scared.
before	Turn the heater off **before** you go to bed. **Before** you go to bed, turn the heater off.
after	They called the firefighters **after** they left the house. **After** they left the house, they called the firefighters.

A clause with when, before, *or* after *is not a complete thought. It is only part of a sentence. What can you say about the position of these clauses in a sentence? When do you need to use a comma with these clauses?*

Grammar Talk: Sentences with *because*

Avalon sees a chiropractor **because** she hurt her back in an accident.

Salvador couldn't afford counseling **because** his deductible was too high.

Maggie went to the optometrist **because** her vision was bad.

Each sentence uses the word because. *Is the underlined "*because *clause" a complete sentence? Is there a comma before* because?

Grammar Talk: Sentences with *must, have to,* and *have got to*

If you want replacement insurance, you **must** pay more.

You **must not** forget to pay your premiums on time.

Insurance companies **don't have to** cover natural disasters.

If someone vandalizes your car, you **have to** report it immediately.

I've got to keep my valuables in a safe place.

Notice that must *is never followed by* to. *How do you form the negatives of* must *and* have to? *Which expression is never used in the negative?*

Vocabulary

These are the words you learned in this unit.

acupuncture
acupuncturist
afford/affordable
agent
antiques
belongings
certificate of deposit (CD)
chiropractic
chiropractor
counseling
counselor
cover
coverage
damage
debt
deductible
destroy
eligible
financial
flood
hail
interest rate
money market account
optometrist
payments
pediatric
pediatrician
penalty
policy
premium
retire/retirement
security
theft
valuables
vandalism
vandalize
vision

Grammar Talk: Superlative Adjectives

I want the high**est** quality video camera that you sell.

I'm looking for the **most** compact cell phone that you have.

I want the remote control that is the easi**est** to use.

The tape recorder had the **best** warranty that I could find.

That store has the **worst** service in town.

When you use a superlative, how many things are you comparing? How do you form the superlative for one- and two-syllable adjectives and adjectives that end in y? *What are the superlative forms for* good *and* bad?

When you compare only two things, you use comparative adjectives.

My computer at work is fast**er** than my computer at home. My new phone is **more** compact than my old phone.

Grammar Talk: *Used to*

Tremaine's dress **used to** fit.

This sweater **used to** be pretty, but now it's faded.

I **used to** shop every weekend.

Did you **use to** shop there?

What does used to *mean? What is the form of the verb after* used to? *In the fourth sentence, why is* use to *in simple form?*

Look at the following sentence. Can you change threw away *to* used to throw away?

Tremaine threw away her ripped jeans yesterday.
What's the difference between the simple past and used to?

Grammar Talk: *One/Ones*

I'm going to buy that shirt. This **one** has a flaw.

These shoes are stained. I need some new **ones.**

Vocabulary

These are the words you learned in this unit.

- aquarium
- blender
- compact
- condition
- crib
- defect
- defective
- durable
- efficient
- exchange
- faded
- flaw
- guarantee
- hamper
- lightweight
- modern
- nightstand
- portable
- powerful
- quality
- recliner
- refund
- rip
- ripped
- scratch
- scratched
- second-hand
- stained
- stroller
- useful
- warranty

Grammar Talk: Gerunds as Subjects and Objects

Smoking at work is prohibited in some states.

She's worried about **going** to jail.

You could receive a fine for **smoking** marijuana.

The words that end in -ing look like verbs, but they are nouns. They are called gerunds. Which ones are subjects and which ones are objects? Notice that a gerund is used after for *and* about.

Grammar Talk: Present Perfect

Present Perfect	Simple Past
He **has been arrested** for drugs three times.	He **was arrested** yesterday.
I **have seen** people drinking in the park.	I **saw** people drinking in the park last weekend.
She **has lost** her enthusiasm for exercise.	
Has she ever **missed** work because of depression?	

The present perfect uses a helping verb and a main verb. Underline the helping verb in each sentence. What is the form of the main verb? In the fourth sentence, what does the word ever *mean?*

The sentences listed under "Simple Past" cannot be changed to present perfect. How are they different from the sentences listed under "Present Perfect"?

Vocabulary

These are the words you learned in this unit.

- abuse
- abusive
- addict
- addicted
- aggressive
- alcoholic
- alcoholism
- allow
- anonymous
- appetite
- arrest
- beat
- corporal punishment
- depressed
- depression
- discipline
- enthusiasm
- enthusiastic
- fine
- forbid
- ground
- harm
- illegal
- irrational
- neglect
- permit
- prohibited
- recover
- sentence
- slap
- spank
- substance
- support
- symptoms

Vocabulary

These are the words you learned in this unit.

- administrator
- appreciate
- approval
- approve
- arrange
- avoid
- block party
- carnival
- committee
- confident
- consider
- dedicated
- donate
- fair
- food bank
- fund-raiser
- generous
- improve
- influence
- issues
- mind
- mural
- opposed
- outgoing
- parade
- persistent
- petition
- punctual
- recommend
- representative
- request
- suggest
- volunteer

Grammar Talk: Verbs Followed by Gerunds

Jenny **doesn't mind** help**ing** with family projects.

She **suggested** call**ing** them.

We **finished** remov**ing** the graffiti yesterday.

She **recommended** go**ing** to the meetings.

I **avoid** work**ing** with my brother.

He **appreciated** gett**ing** help.

Marlene **stopped** work**ing** at age 62.

They **considered** paint**ing** a mural.

Look at the verb that comes before the gerund in each sentence. These verbs cannot be followed by the infinitive or simple form.

Grammar Talk: Present Perfect with *for* and *since*

He has volunteered at the food bank **for** three months.

She has donated her time to the school **for** many years.

He has participated in the multicultural carnival **for** the last two years.

My neighbors and I have worked to improve the neighborhood **since** June.

I have arranged all of the meetings **since** 2001.

He has been outgoing **since** he was a child.

Find the words for *and* since *in each sentence. Which word is followed by a specific time? Which word is followed by a length of time?*

Grammar Talk: Future with *will* and *be going to*

I'm going to study at the library tomorrow.

I think **I'll study** at the library tomorrow.

I'll help you study.

I'll come home early.

We use will *and* be going to *for planned activities.*
We use will *to make offers and promises.*

You can write contractions of will *and* be *with pronouns, but not with nouns.*

Grammar Talk: Polite Requests with Modals

These questions are direct:

Where is the reference section?

What does this word mean?

These questions are more polite:

Could you please tell me **where** the reference section is?

Would you please tell me **what** this word means?

Compare the direct question to the polite question.

Vocabulary

These are the words you learned in this unit.

add
admission
advantage
article
biography
career
consistent
distract
distraction
documentary
drop
due
earn
enroll
enrollment
fees
fulfilling
inconsistent
lifelong learning
meaningful
nonfiction
opportunity
overdue
periodical
practical
priority
reference
register
registration
renew
requirements
research
resource
routine
schedule
tuition

Grammar Talk: Present Perfect Continuous

Rania **has been sewing** for many years.

The employees **have been using** outdated machines for a long time.

The company **hasn't been updating** their equipment.

Rania **has been feeling** nervous about the new machines at work.

The present perfect continuous is used to describe actions that began in the past and are still happening now or have just stopped. A present perfect continuous verb has three parts.

Grammar Talk: Present/Future Sentences with *If*

If I **put** this in the microwave, it **will explode.**

If he **doesn't check** the answering machine, he **won't know** when I'm coming home.

I'll be late if I **don't figure out** how to set the alarm clock.

I **won't bother** you anymore if you **teach** me how to use this program.

Which verb is in the part of the sentence with if, *the present verb or the future verb? When do sentences with* if *need a comma?*

Vocabulary

These are the words you learned in this unit.

- adapt
- adjust
- affect
- bar code
- clockwise
- confront
- cope
- counterclockwise
- display
- effect
- hang up
- mandatory
- network
- operate
- outdated
- overcome
- press
- program
- pros and cons
- react
- reaction
- remove
- resist
- scanning
- set
- start over
- touch-screen
- train
- turn
- update
- workshop

Answer Key

UNIT 1
Lesson 1

Exercise B
2. How long <u>does</u> the ceramics class last? It <u>lasts</u> for one month.
3. How much <u>does</u> the lecture <u>cost</u>? It <u>costs</u> $10.
4. Where <u>is</u> the martial arts class? It <u>is</u> in room 25.

Exercise D
1. What time <u>does</u> the swimming class start?
2. The gymnastics class <u>doesn't</u> meet on July 4th.
3. How much <u>does</u> the class <u>cost</u>?
4. When <u>does</u> the class finish? *or* When <u>is</u> the class <u>finished</u>?

Lesson 2

Exercise A
2. Do you participate in sports?
3. Does she have conflicts at home?
4. Are you a confident person? *or* You are a confident person.
5. She has confidence, but I don't.
6. The Senior Center fulfills many needs.

Exercise B
1. don't
2. is
3. isn't
4. doesn't
5. does
6. do
7. aren't

Exercise C
1. generations
2. disrespectful
3. inflexible
4. responsible
5. respectful
6. flexible
7. unreliable

Lesson 3

Exercise A
1. c   2. a   3. d   4. b

Exercise B
1. S, M, S
2. S, S, M
3. M, S, S
4. S, M, S

UNIT 2
Lesson 1

Exercise A
1. wink
2. shrug
3. bow
4. slouch
5. stare
6. whisper
7. nudge

Exercise B
1. left
2. got
3. ran
4. was carrying
5. threw
6. thought
7. was sitting
8. heard

Exercise C
• making a circle with the thumb and index finger and showing the palm
• gesture for "come here" with the palm facing up, sometimes with the index finger extended
• gesture for "come here" with the palm facing down
• pointing at things with the index finger
• using the chin to point
• putting feet on a stool when sitting
• crossing one foot over a knee

Lesson 2

Exercise A
    I was so mad last week when I went to Lee's Dry Cleaners to pick up my jacket. I gave the clerk my ticket, and she looked for my jacket. After a few minutes, she said, "I'm sorry, but your jacket won't be ready until Thursday." I couldn't believe it because I knew she told me that it would be ready on Tuesday. I started to yell at her. I said, "You told me Tuesday, not Thursday." The manager came out when I was yelling. He said, "Is there a problem that I can help you with?" So I told him about the mix-up. He said, "Pardon me for the misunderstanding." Then he looked at the ticket and said, "You can see that Thursday is circled, not Tuesday." I was so embarrassed when I found out that it was my fault. I said, "Oh, you're right. I apologize for yelling. I didn't look at the ticket." He was very nice about it. He said, "Don't worry, we'll call you when your jacket is ready. Again, please forgive us for the misunderstanding."

Exercise B
2. I gave the clerk my ticket.
3. She said, "I'm sorry, but your jacket won't be ready until Thursday."
4. I was yelling.
5. The manager came out.
6. He looked at the ticket.

Exercise D

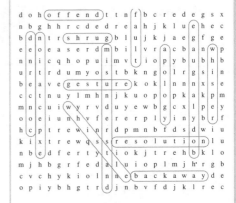

UNIT 3
Lesson 1

Exercise A
2. Did he knock over the lamp?
3. Were they suspicious of him?
4. Did the little girl fracture her arm?
5. Did the doctor treat the injury?
6. Did she get a shock from the old cord?
7. Was the plant poisonous?

Exercise B
2. What did Miguel look for? He looked for the first-aid kit.
3. Where did he find it? He found it in the bottom of a drawer.
4. What did Miguel decide to do? He decided to make his workplace safer.

Answer Key

Exercise C

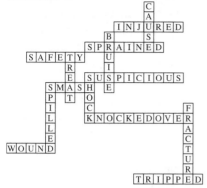

Lesson 2

Exercise A

2. f	4. h	6. c	8. g
3. a	5. e	7. b	

1. unplúg
2. put awáy
3. smóke detector
4. repláce
5. plug ín
6. lock úp
7. escápe route
8. fíre extinguisher

Exercise B

1. safe
2. injury
3. prevent
4. cause
5. poisons
6. poisonous
7. slips
8. rob
9. prevention

Exercise C

2, 3, 5, 1, 4

Exercise D

1. Juan Salazar woke up when he heard an explosion.
2. Claudia Salazar was very frightened before her son was rescued.
3. The boy went to the hospital after he was injured.
4. The parents ran out of the building before their son got out.
5. The firefighters arrived after the neighbor called them.

Lesson 3

Exercise A

1. kept an eye on
2. stranger
3. break into
4. witness
5. victim

Exercise C

1. held
2. stranger
3. lock up
4. suspect

UNIT 4
Lesson 1

Exercise A

2. They had to borrow money to pay their medical bills.
3. He thought they couldn't afford the premiums.
4. They enrolled in the health plan because it would be better to make small payments every month.
5. Olivia wants to see a chiropractor because she has neck pain.

Exercise B

1. People under age 50 and their children under age 18 are eligible.
2. The policy covers emergency health care for accident and sudden illness.
3. Monthly payments are $100.
4. The yearly premium is $1,200.
5. The deductible is $300 per year.
6. The agent is Sal Mosqueda.

Lesson 2

Exercise A

1. must not
2. have to
3. don't have to
4. doesn't have to

Exercise B

1. e	3. a	5. c	7. h
2. g	4. d	6. b	8. f

Exercise D

Olivia called the insurance agent because she wanted to find out about homeowners insurance. When she talked to the agent, he also gave her some information about life insurance. She learned that there are two kinds of life insurance. *Term* insurance is not very expensive when you are young, but it gets expensive when you are older. *Whole-life* insurance is more expensive because it lasts your whole life. The insurance agent wanted Olivia to buy life insurance, but she didn't think she needed it. She and Victor are both working, and they don't have children yet. She said to the insurance agent, "Maybe I will talk to you about life insurance after we have children."

Lesson 3

Exercise A

1. interest rate
2. certificate of deposit
3. money market
4. penalty

Exercise C

1. We had to fix the roof because the hail damaged it.
   or Because the hail damaged it, we had to fix the roof.
   or Because the hail damaged the roof, we had to fix it.
2. We are enjoying our retirement because we prepared for it.
   or Are we enjoying our retirement because we prepared for it?
   or Because we prepared for our retirement, we are enjoying it.
   or Because we prepared for it, we are enjoying our retirement.
3. Everybody would like to have financial security.
   or Would everybody like to have financial security?

UNIT 5
Lesson 1

Exercise B

2. d	3. c	4. a	5. c	6. b

Answer Key

Lesson 2

Exercise A
1. Tremaine didn't want the dress because it wasn't perfect.
   or Because it wasn't perfect, Tremaine didn't want the dress.
   or Because the dress wasn't perfect, Tremaine didn't want it.
2. Tremaine changed her mind and decided to buy the dress.
3. Tremaine and Gail went to Second-Hand Rose yesterday.
   or Gail and Tremaine went to Second-Hand Rose yesterday.
   or Yesterday, Tremaine and Gail went to Second-Hand Rose.
   or Yesterday, Gail and Tremaine went to Second-Hand Rose.
4. They found a beautiful dress that had a flaw.
   or A beautiful dress that they found had a flaw.
   or They found that a beautiful dress had a flaw.
5. Gail showed Tremaine that the defect was small.

Exercise B
1. rip
2. scratch
3. guarantee
4. exchange
5. refund

Exercise D
- Before Tremaine <u>was</u> born, Gail and Trevor <u>bought</u> most of their clothes at the mall.
- They <u>liked</u> shopping at the big department stores.
- They <u>purchased</u> their first sofa on credit.
- In fact, they <u>paid</u> for many things with credit.
- They <u>made</u> small payments every month.
- After a while, they <u>had</u> a lot of debt to pay.
- So they <u>decided</u> to use cash for all their purchases.
- They are sorry that they <u>spent</u> so much money on interest.

1. Before Tremaine was born, Gail and Trevor used to buy all of their clothes at the mall.
2. They used to like shopping at the big department stores.
3. In fact, they used to pay for many things with credit.
4. They used to make small payments every month.
5. They are sorry that they used to spend so much money on interest.

Lesson 3

Exercise A
blender, stroller, nightstand, crib, hamper, aquarium, recliner

Exercise B
1. c   2. b   3. c   4. c

Exercise C
1. than
2. most
3. best
4. the
5. than
6. more
7. cheaper

UNIT 6
Lesson 1

Exercise A
1. The illegal substance was marijuana.
2. The policeman arrested John for drinking alcohol and for smoking marijuana.
3. The fine was $300.
4. John's sentence was two months in a home for teenagers.
5. Making phone calls after 6 P.M. was prohibited at the home for teenagers.

Lesson 2

Exercise A
2. d   3. c   4. a   5. f   6. b

2. Permitting children to use the Internet alone can be dangerous. For example, a 14-year-old girl was killed by a man she met online.
3. If you hit children when you are angry, you might hurt them. For example, I know a boy who slapped his father. The father was so upset that he beat the boy.
4. Grounding your teenager is a good way to discipline. For example, after my 16-year-old had to stay home all weekend, he changed his behavior.
5. Neglecting your children's needs can cause emotional harm. For example, if a mother rarely pays attention to her children, they may be unhappy.
6. Children have trouble learning at schools that allow corporal punishment. For example, my teacher used to hit students on the hand with a ruler. We were afraid of her!

Exercise B
1. get involved
2. abusive
3. alcoholic

Lesson 3

Exercise A
1. lethargic
2. appetite
3. enthusiastic
4. enthusiasm
5. aggressive
6. depression
7. reckless
8. irrational

Exercise B
1. heard *or* have heard
2. saw
3. smelled *or* have smelled
4. spoken
5. had
6. asked
7. have tried
8. met
9. started
10. told
11. has gone

Answer Key

UNIT 7
Lesson 1

Exercise A
2. She volunteered to work in the classroom.
3. She appreciated Marlene's offer to help.
4. She recommended that Marlene call someone on the school carnival committee.
5. She requested Marlene's help with the decorations.
6. No, she didn't mind helping with the decorations.

Lesson 2

Exercise A
1. moved   5. visits
2. went   6. hasn't worked
3. missed   7. helps *or* has helped
4. met   8. has learned

Exercise B
1. issue   5. approval
2. opposed   6. representative
3. petition   7. influence
4. approved

Lesson 3

Exercise B
1. for   3. since   5. since
2. for   4. since

Exercise C
1. has been; was
2. was; had *or* has had
3. helped *or* has helped; arranged
4. have done; planned
5. has never traveled; went
6. has always loved; planted
7. has taken; took

Exercise D
1. mural   4. carnival
2. committee   5. parade
3. fund-raiser   6. block party

UNIT 8
Lesson 1

Exercise A
1. will spend *or* am going to spend
2. will help
3. am going to visit
4. is going to fix
5. will do
6. am going to be

Exercise B
1. c   2. d   3. a   4. e   5. b

Lesson 2

Exercise A
1. f   3. g   5. h   7. j   9. c
2. d   4. i   6. b   8. a   10. e

Exercise B
1. reference   4. documentary
2. research   5. advantage
3. look up   6. opportunity

Exercise D
1. b   2. c   3. d

Lesson 3

Exercise A
1. drop   5. requirements
2. admissions   6. fees *or* tuition
3. enroll   7. tuition *or* fees
4. earn   8. never too late

Exercise B

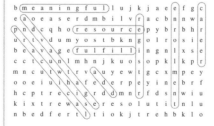

Exercise C
2. Do you know what days the class meets?
3. Could you tell me when registration begins?
4. Do you know when children's story hour is?

UNIT 9
Lesson 1

Exercise A
2. She has been researching information for two months.
3. She has been researching an Internet business selling children's clothes.
4. She won't be able to start her business right away because she has been spending so much time at work.

Exercise B
1. d   2. e   3. a   4. b   5. c

Exercise C
1. Rania's boss wanted to update the equipment.
2. Her co-workers reacted the same way.
3. But her boss said, "You will adapt."
   or Her boss said, "But you will adapt."
   or "But you will adapt," said her boss.
4. He said, "New machines will have a positive effect on production."
   or "New machines will have a positive effect on production," he said.
5. They weren't looking forward to the mandatory training.
6. He announced a workshop.
7. Rania's reaction wasn't very positive.
8. But employees always have to deal with change.
9. They resisted it for a long time.
   or For a long time, they resisted it.

Lesson 2

Exercise A
1. laying off   4. bar codes
2. network   5. touch-screen
3. scanning

Answer Key

Exercise B

1. has used *or* has been using
2. have put *or* have been putting
3. have had
4. hasn't been
5. has laid off *or* has been laying off
6. haven't coped *or* haven't been coping

Lesson 2

Exercise B

1. wanted
2. beeping
3. was helping
4. beeping
5. were staring
6. tried
7. will be
8. knows
9. have been trying
10. have never had
11. gave
12. haven't bought
13. am going to buy

Exercise C